A Conceptual Approach to Teaching Children About Science, Technology, and Society

Brenda J. Gustafson, Ph.D.
Dougal A.G. MacDonald, Ph.D.

Ripon Publishing 2005
A Division of Ripon Consulting Ltd.
ISBN: 6-0153-0014-0

Also available by the same authors: Companion Manual to A Conceptual Approach to Teaching Children About Science, Technology, and Society (2005).
Ripon Publishing: A Division of Ripon Consulting Ltd.
ISBN: 6-0153-0015-9

A discount is provided when ordering the combined publication package, which includes this textbook and the accompanying companion manual.
Contact: RiponPub@telus.net

[Library of Congress Info]
ISBN: 6-0153-0014-0

The Web addresses cited in this text were current as of June 2005, unless otherwise noted.

Acquisitions Editor: Dr. G. J. Fishburne; **Developmental Editor:** Dr. G. J. Fishburne; **Copyeditor:** Dr. G. J. Fishburne; **Cover Designer:** Chad Spears; **Text Layout:** Sara Bartisch

Printed in Edmonton, Alberta, Canada by Dial Printing Inc.

Ripon Publishing
RipPub@Telus.net

About the Authors

Dr. Brenda Gustafson began her career as an elementary school teacher and is now a Professor of Elementary Science Education at the University of Alberta. Dr. Gustafson has been awarded the Faculty of Education's Undergraduate Teaching award for her distinguished teaching and has presented many workshops and seminars for elementary teachers. Her research has focused on teaching science and design technology in elementary classrooms. She has published in academic journals such as the Journal of Technology Education, Research in Science Education, the Journal of Qualitative Studies in Education, the Canadian Journal of Science, Mathematics and Technology Education, Research in Science and Technology Education, the International Journal of Technology and Design Education, and the Alberta Journal of Education Research. She has presented her research at numerous annual conferences such as those associated with the Canadian Society for the Study of Education, the American Educational Research Association, The International Technology Education Association, and the National Association for Research in Science Teaching.

Dr. Dougal MacDonald is an award-winning full-time sessional instructor at the University of Alberta where he currently teaches elementary science methods. A science educator for over 17 years, he is known for his enthusiasm, sense of humour, and ability to meaningfully integrate theory and practice. Dougal's main research interests are constructivism, the conceptual analysis of teaching, the nature of science, Aboriginal education, and design technology. His research has been presented at international conferences and published in international academic journals.

Acknowledgements

For my parents, George and Margaret Gustafson, who when I was a child gave me a chemistry set, microscope, and crystal radio kit that sparked my early interest in science and technology. And my academic mentor, Dr. Margaret McNay, who encouraged and nurtured my interest in science and technology education with children.

Brenda Gustafson

Dougal MacDonald would like to thank his parents Ian and Billie MacDonald, his children Ellen and Stuart MacDonald, his mentor Douglas A. Roberts, and, especially, Leslie Sharpe, for their much appreciated inspiration, guidance, and support.

Special Note

A portion of the proceeds from this book will be donated to undergraduate student awards in education.

Disclaimer: Safety and Teaching Progressions

All the activities contained in this textbook have been identified as developmentally appropriate for children and youth, providing recognized teaching progressions are followed, and recognized safety procedures adhered to and employed. Before engaging in any of the activities, or teaching any of the activities identified in this textbook, the reader must be familiar with and cognizant of both recognized safety considerations and developmentally appropriate teaching progressions, and must follow these safety considerations and teaching progressions. Hence, anyone who engages in any of the activities contained in this textbook does so completely at their own risk. Anyone who engages in any of the activities contained or suggested in this textbook takes full responsibility for any and all effects as a result of engaging in these activities. No blame, fault, or liability whatsoever of any kind can be made against the authors of this publication or the publishing company. Implementation of any of the activities or ideas contained in this textbook should in all cases be preceded by a close review of the specific requirements and circumstances associated with the teaching, learning, and/or performing situation. Each person using the activities and ideas contained in this textbook assumes the risks associated with the implementation and customization of the activities and ideas. The authors, editors, and publishing company make no representations or warranties, either expressed or implied, as to any matter including the condition, quality, or freedom from error of the activities, ideas, and content contained in this textbook. Each person using the activities, ideas, and content assumes the risk of defects or inaccuracies in the textbook as supplied by the authors, editors, and publishing company. The authors, editor, and publishing company will have no liability, consequential damages, special damages, punitive damages, or otherwise which might arise from the use by any one of the activities, ideas, and content material contained within this textbook.

Safety Guidelines

When teaching or engaging people in the activities and ideas contained in this textbook, recognized safety guidelines must be followed. Check and follow the safety guidelines policy and procedures applicable to the school district, municipality, county, province, state, and country where the teaching of the activities and ideas contained in this textbook will occur. As noted above, when people participate in activities there is a risk of injury. Therefore teachers must be careful to provide an adequate standard of care for the people they are teaching; that is, they must create safe learning environments. Prior to teaching or engaging people in the activities and ideas contained in this textbook, teachers must be able to answer each of the following five questions with a 'yes' :

1. Is the activity suitable to the age, cognitive, emotional, and physical condition of the participants? In other words is it developmentally appropriate?

2. Will the participants be taught through correct teaching progressions, and do the teacher's unit and lesson plans indicate and support this?

3. Are the apparatus, equipment, and materials developmentally appropriate, suitably arranged for a safe learning environment, and in good condition?

4. Will the activity be supervised properly?

5. Has a 'risk' assessment been made to consider the potential risks associated with the planned activities? And have 'safety' steps been taken to reduce or minimize these risks?

Teaching in Alberta Schools

The following 'safety' guideline is recommended and must be followed when teaching or engaging children and youth in any type of physical activity in Alberta Schools in Canada:

Safety Guidelines
For Physical Activity in Alberta Schools
ISBN 0-9699567-6-2

Web site: *www.med.ualberta.ca/acicr*
This web site provides links to resources (safety guidelines, policies, procedures, recommendations, etc.) across Canada and the United States.
Many resource recommendations are available on line through the web site, including the following documents:

Safety Guidelines for Physical Activity in Alberta Schools
L'activite physique dans les ecole de l'Alberta (available in electronic version only)
ACICR Bicycle Education Program Inventory
Thesaurus of Injury Prevention Terminology
Safety Guidelines for Secondary Interschool Athletics in Alberta
The Alberta Directory for Emergency Medical and Acute Care Services
Alberta Education: Safety in the Science Classroom
www.education.gov.ab.ca

Inquiries can be addressed to:
Alberta Centre for Injury Control & Research
University of Alberta, 4075 EDC,
8308 – 114 Street, Edmonton, Alberta, Canada T6G 2V2
Tel: 780-492-7154

Contents

Preface
How This Book Is Organized

Aim of the Textbook

The aim of the textbook is to help you become an effective beginning elementary school science teacher. We have organized this textbook and companion manual to encourage you to learn and understand some of the basic ideas associated with teaching Science, Technology, and Society (STS). We believe the ideas and approach represented in this textbook and accompanying Companion Manual represent the best current thinking about the what, why, and how of science education, and that you should use these ideas to organize your thoughts and guide your teaching practices. We have written and organized the chapters of this textbook and the Companion Manual with your learning in mind. To help you learn and understand the concepts, ideas, and content material we have organized the textbook and Companion Manual into a number of sections, highlighted headings, and provided a number of problem solving activities. More details on how best to learn the textbook and Companion Manual material appears below under the heading 'Helping You to Learn'.

Chapter Content

The following paragraphs provide a brief explanation of the content and basic ideas contained in each of the book's chapters.

- *Elementary science teachers' actions are influenced by their beliefs about how children learn and by their views about, and perceptions of the nature of science and technology.* Your teaching strategies (e.g., how you talk to your students, how you structure your science lessons) and the criteria you use to select teaching resources are a number of future actions that will be influenced by how you think children learn and what you think science and technology are. In this textbook, at the beginning of each chapter, we ask you to examine your existing ideas (the "Thinking About Your Existing Ideas" feature box), as part of developing your understanding of basic ideas about learning and about STS that now influence science education. In chapters 1, 2, 3, 4, 5, and 6 our intention is to help you broaden your view of scientific inquiry, technological problem solving and STS decision-making and help you understand how learning theories (in particular, theories that view learning as a constructive process) have profound practical implications for classroom teaching. We will refer you to the Companion Manual activities and to other information to provide a more concrete picture of some of these implications.

- *Elementary science teachers should begin by developing a framework of teaching goals for moving children towards understanding concepts, constructing connections between concepts, and developing the right skills and attitudes.* Ideas about how children learn and about the nature of science and technology should influence the way you plan science lessons. In Chapter 3 we ask you to think about the concepts, skills, and attitudes that underpin many science and technology programs and about how to construct a framework of goals (i.e., a conceptual framework – see Companion Manual Part D). This emphasis on the important knowledge that underpins classroom lessons (concepts) and the additional need to help children develop appropriate skills and attitudes is what we mean by a conceptual approach to teaching children. Chapter 5 discusses the importance of a planning framework and the levels of planning commonly expected in schools (e.g., year plans, unit plans, and daily lesson plans).

- *Elementary science teachers should use a variety of teaching strategies in order to support scientific inquiry, technological problem solving, and STS decision-making.* Chapter 4 begins by noting the importance of managing ideas and managing children. With respect to managing ideas, we will introduce you to a variety of teaching strategies linked to constructivist learning that are recommended for use in elementary school science classrooms. We emphasize that your pedagogical content knowledge about how to teach particular content, should determine your choice of strategies.

- *Elementary science teachers need to know how to structure classroom space, time, and resources in order to create a flexible, supportive learning environment for children.* With respect to managing children, Chapter 4 presents general teaching and instructional strategies, and emphasizes the idea that the more effective you are at managing your ideas, the less you will have to manage children. We encourage you to think about strategies you can use to create a supportive, safe, and caring classroom environment for your students, and we provide you with lists of materials and teaching resources commonly used in elementary school science programs, along with a list of suppliers (see Appendices C and D).

- *Elementary science teachers should use a variety of assessment tools on an ongoing basis to gather information about children's progress, and they should use this information to help children learn.* In Chapter 6 we look at the purposes and importance of assessment. We explore concept, skill, and attitude assessment, as well as the limits of atomized assessment. We discuss assessment before, during, and after teaching, and ask you to consider the merits of a variety of assessment tools. Chapter 6 also includes a brief commentary on the use and misuse of standardized achievement tests. We ask you to stay informed about science education trends and developments and to keep in mind this critical question: "Whose interests are served by this particular trend or development?"

- *Elementary science teachers need to know and understand major science concepts and children's ideas about these concepts in order to plan activities forchildren.* In the Companion Manual, we feature special pedagogical apparatus designed to help you become familiar with science concepts, reflect upon children's alternative conceptions related to those concepts, and formulate ideas about typical science and technology activities for children.

- *Elementary science teachers need to be lifelong learners in order to integrate and extend their knowledge of children, science, and pedagogy.* Research shows that your recall of the good ideas about teaching children science from your curriculum and instruction courses may fade as you encounter the complex world of teaching science in schools. Concerns about the availability of supplies, working with parents, behavior management, curriculum standards, assessment expectations, and participating in school life can overwhelm even a well-prepared, enthusiastic beginning science teacher. All teachers should, therefore, make a commitment to stay in touch with ideas about science teaching encountered during their preservice years and continue their professional development throughout their careers. To help you develop this approach, we have listed questions at the end of each chapter (in the "Ideas to Think About When Teaching Science, Technology, and Society") for you to reflect on during your practicum placements and when you are teaching. The questions are also designed to help you make theory-practice connections. At the end of each chapter, we also provide a short list of selected readings and websites related to the chapter content. This information illustrates and extends upon important chapter ideas and will help you develop a more in-depth understanding of science teaching. In Appendix D and in the Companion Manual (Part E) we include a list of sources of professional support to help you during your teaching career.

- *Elementary science teachers need practice in designing and conducting investigations and experiments.* In the Companion Manual Part B, we have included activities intended to help you gain practice in typical investigations and experiments. Although your instructor might not be able to include all these activities in the course, we encourage you to try all activities as a way of broadening your understanding of STS education. Finally, before conducting similar activities with children, you should always consider and view safety as a priority issue. The textbook chapters and Companion Manual emphasize safety issues throughout.

Helping You to Learn

At the beginning of each chapter is a feature box identifying 'learning outcomes'. These feature boxes identify key learning objectives and key concepts associated with the content material of each chapter. Throughout each chapter major headings highlight important content, and questions are posed to get the reader to self-reflect and think about major issues and concepts related to the teaching of science, technology, and society. The book follows a 'constructivist' approach to learning, involving readers in problem solving activities and the construction of their own knowledge. Toward the end of each chapter is a 'summary ideas' section where key concepts and ideas covered in the chapter are summarized for the reader. This is followed with sections on how to 'make productive connections' and 'ideas to think about when teaching science, technology, and society.' Finally, at the end of each chapter is a section on selected readings and resources to help teach elementary school science, technology, and society. This is followed with a comprehensive listing and brief review of Internet web sites to provide further support and resource material pertinent to chapter content and related to children, science, technology, and society. Throughout the textbook cross-reference is made to the Companion Manual where a variety of exercises, problems, and activities can be found that relate to key learning objectives and concepts presented in each chapter of this textbook. The reader is encouraged to complete these activities to reinforce and enhance the content material presented. Completing the chapter readings and activities provided in the Companion Manual will help develop the necessary knowledge, skills, and attributes to become an effective teacher of elementary school science, which is the major aim of this textbook.

Chapter 1
Introduction to Teaching Children About Science, Technology, and Society

Learning Objectives

In this chapter, you should learn:

- Why science, technology, and society are connected.
- How science and technology are defined.
- How scientific and technological literacy are defined.
- Why we should teach children about science, technology, and society.

Thinking About Your Existing Ideas

Write down your answers to the following questions. After you complete this chapter, revisit your answers. Which of your ideas remained the same and which changed? How did they change, and what do you believe caused the changes?

- How do you think your beliefs about science and technology will influence your approach to teaching science?
- What does the term "science" mean to you? What comes to mind when you think of science?
- What would someone who is "scientifically literate" know and be able to do?
- What does the term "technology" mean to you? What comes to mind when you think of technology?
- What would someone who is "technologically literate" know and be able to do?
- How do science, technology, and society relate to each other?

"These are interesting ideas and I've learned a lot, but could you just tell us the way to teach science?" A preservice teacher enrolled in an introductory science curriculum and instruction course asked this question, giving the distinct impression that he thought the professor (one of the authors) had been holding out for the first four weeks of the course. His desire for a "one size fits all" method for teaching science was understandable, particularly with an upcoming practicum. Preservice teachers want to do a good job and want to teach science in a way that will promote children's learning. And practicum reports about preservice teachers' performance are important documents used to support job applications.

How should the preservice teacher's question be answered? The history of science education shows that people's ideas about how to teach science and even about how to organize science programs are very much influenced by what they believe about what science is, how children learn science, and even why science should be taught. These beliefs, in turn, are very much influenced by time and place–by people's social, cultural, and political context. Thus, over the years, there have been many different beliefs about the best way to teach science. Nevertheless, we believe that some instructional strategies are more promising than others, and, we will examine those strategies and help you become familiar with them. This was the answer given the preservice teacher and it seemed to encourage him, while also hinting at the complexity of science teaching. The complexity will gradually become clearer as you complete your preservice courses and continue into your teaching career.

At present, you are beginning an introductory science curriculum and instruction course, but you are also continuing a journey you began as a child, when you first wondered about clouds, leaves, water, and other aspects of the natural world. The explanations you invented then to make sense of these phenomena have remained with you, maybe to be modified as you encountered science both in and out of school. Now you have the opportunity not only to revisit children's ideas about science, including your own, but also to consider science from the perspective of a preservice teacher. As you use this textbook (along with the Companion Manual) to help you think about science and children, reflect on your own past journey through science and how ideas and impressions formed during that journey influence your beliefs.

This initial chapter is framed around three basic questions concerning science, technology, and society. By considering these questions, you will begin to see the big picture of science, technology, society and teaching:

- What is science?
- What is technology and how is it being linked to science programs?
- What are we trying to accomplish by teaching science, technology, and society in elementary classrooms?

Thinking about these and other questions will help you form ideas about how you will teach science in the future, help you better understand your own past science experiences, and give you a sense of where science education might be going. Through interacting with this textbook, and Companion Manual, you will construct a deeper understanding of the profession you are preparing to enter and you will begin to acquire the professional knowledge of a science educator— knowledge of children, teaching, curriculum, educational contexts, and how to interpret and transform subject matter for children.

Thinking About Teaching Children About Science, Technology, and Society

You might have been surprised to read the title for this textbook because you are enrolled in a *science* curriculum and instruction course. Why do topics such as 'technology' and 'society' appear in a science course textbook?

During the past three decades, science educators have tended to agree that it is difficult to study science without recognizing how it is inevitably related to technology. A common myth is that this relationship can be reduced to "Technology is applied science", however, this is an oversimplification and is historically inaccurate. Instead, the relationship between science and technology is much more complex and it is apparent to science educators that conversations about science should also include technology (see later in this chapter for a more complete discussion of the relationship between science and technology).

Discussions about society arise when studying science and technology as both are embedded in the social context. For example, the automobile (an example of a technology that incorporates many science concepts) has changed society in many ways, from the creation of assembly line manufacturing to the proliferation of fast food drive-in outlets, while at the same time society has changed the automobile by demanding new designs and more powerful engines.

In the 1980s, an approach to teaching science emerged called Science-Technology-Society or STS (also called Science-Technology-Society-Environment or STSE) and focused around social issues with a scientific or technological aspect (e.g., waste disposal, nuclear power, genetic engineering, and stem cell research). One important influence on the rise of STS was the growth of the environmental movement that took a more problematic view of the effects of science and technology on human society. An STS approach views science and technology in their social context and is part of a general trend to expand science education beyond a focus solely on science knowledge.

In the 1990s, authors of science education standards in Canada (*Common Framework of Science Learning Outcomes*, Council of Ministers of Education, Canada, 1997) and the United States (*National Science Education Standards*, National Research Council, 1996) acknowledged the links between science, technology, and society by including all three aspects in their learning goals. Thus, programs of study in North America include opportunities for students to learn about science, technology, and society.

Teachers have taken different approaches to teaching students about science, technology, and society. Some teachers focus their science units on problems such as waste disposal and each lesson within the unit is intended to help children consider elements of science, technology, and society. Other teachers interested in helping students to think about waste disposal might design a unit that has lessons that could typically be called science lessons, and then complement these lessons by others that have more of a technology focus. Also included within the unit would be lessons that focus more on the societal implications of waste disposal. Both of these approaches to planning a STS unit would be acceptable as they include opportunities for children to consider science, technology, and society.

Other topics mentioned in programs of studies could also be adapted to include elements of science, technology, and society. For example, a unit on Electricity could include typical science investigations using light bulbs, batteries, and wires along with opportunities to design and build model electricity powered vehicles (technology). Students could discuss what societal values are reflected in our need to develop sources of electrical power, the impact our need for electricity has on the environment, and the possibilities of alternative means of generating electricity. Students could also consider actions they might take to reduce their own electrical consumption (e.g., turning off the lights when leaving a room). At the conclusion of the unit, students would have considered the interconnections among science, technology, and society while working within the context of electricity.

Connecting science with technology and society is seen as a more authentic way of teaching science to children. Through taking this wider view of science, students can begin to develop both scientific and technological literacy (see later in this chapter for more details about how literacy is defined).

Why Should Teachers Reflect on Their Existing Beliefs About Science and Technology?

In order to teach STS effectively and plan productive experiences for your future students, it is important to begin by reflecting on your beliefs about science, technology, and society and the potential impact you will have upon your students' beliefs about STS.

You may at first think that reflecting on your beliefs about the nature of science (NOS) and the nature of technology (NOT) is an academic exercise with no relation to classroom teaching. However, there are a number of reasons why it is important:

- Your existing ideas about science and technology can affect how you think about science and technology in both your preservice and professional years.

- Your existing ideas may be identical to, conflict with, or approximate those ideas presented in this text as well as those ideas considered appropriate by science educators and scientists.

- Your perceptions of science and technology can influence how you talk about science and technology with your students, how you interpret science curricula, how you plan lessons, how you teach, and how you assess student learning.

- You can play an important role in helping your future students construct perceptions of what science and technology are, what contributions science and technology provide, and perhaps the degree of confidence students should place in science and technology.

- Understanding science and technology is an important aspect of scientific and technological literacy and of being an educated person.

Therefore, it is important to ask yourself, "What images of science and technology do I have?" What images of science and technology will I convey when I teach science to children?" You then need to ask yourself, "Are the images of science and technology that I am conveying in my classroom authentic images?"

While your beliefs about the natures of science and technology can affect both how you teach and what your students learn, the relationship may be indirect. We cannot accurately predict how a teacher with a particular view of science or technology will teach or what her students will come to understand. Classrooms are complex places and other factors also influence teaching and learning, including classroom management, curriculum goals, institutional conditions, students' ideas, and teaching experience. In addition, your degree of understanding of science and technology and the priority you place upon it as a goal of teaching are important considerations.

You should also be aware that when we teach science and technology we often convey an image of those pursuits implicitly (an image we are unaware of) rather than explicitly. Think of your own experiences as a student. It is quite possible that when you carried out investigations in one of your science classes you were requested to write up your results in a specific format. Although not actually stated (or intended) by your teacher, this may have implied to you that all science investigations are done the same way and that there is something called the scientific method that is followed recipe-like by all scientists, even though this is not the case. Since teaching conveys an image of science and technology even when this is not done intentionally, it is advantageous for you to be aware of what that image should be and to convey it consciously rather than unconsciously. (To get a sense of your view of scientists, go to the Companion Manual and do Textbook Activity 1.1.)

Thinking About Science

What Is Science?

Look back at your response to the question "What does the term 'science' mean to you?" When we ask preservice teachers this question, we usually receive a variety of responses, such as:

- Science is discovery, research, and explanation.
- Science is facts covering a broad spectrum of subjects—biology, chemistry, physics, and so on.
- Science is a way to describe things in nature and explain how they work.
- Science comes from our need for certainty; it is based on rational, logical deduction.
- Science is factual study, as opposed to philosophical study.
- Science is the search for truth through objective research.
- Science is getting to know about things by testing hypotheses and reproducing results.

These responses vary to a degree, but overall they indicate that our preservice teachers view science as a logical, factual, infallible search for truth. What might influence them to think this way? Clearly, their views are influenced by the messages about science they have received during their lives. When we ask preservice teachers where they got their ideas about science, they recall a variety of sources, such as:

- School experiences (e.g., science lessons, teachers' portrayals of science).
- The media (e.g., television, newspapers, magazines, radio).
- Family members and friends.
- Hobbies.

For example, news reports about happenings in science frequently refer to new discoveries, the credibility of objective scientific data versus anecdotal data, and the need for more research. Reading these media reports could persuade people to view science as logical, factual, and infallible, particularly if they have heard similar messages in the classroom or from friends and family. Another example involves science textbooks, which are organized according to the logic of the subject, explaining the main ideas and providing supporting information that helps confirm these ideas. Sutton (1989) observes that to many readers, "textbooks seem to be just stores of facts, and their dominance in people's experience at school leaves an image of science as just a lot of information" (p. 153). Given these and other powerful influences, it's hardly surprising that most people view science the same way, but how do scientists themselves view science?

A good way to understand how scientists view and do science is to read books by scientists and philosophers of science. Doing so might well lead you to reconsider what science is and to question some of the images of science within our culture. During your reading, you should also think about what you were doing as a young child when you wondered about the natural world, made observations, and used your existing knowledge to construct explanations. You may be surprised to see how closely the processes that scientists use when "doing science" mirror the processes that children use to explain things.

Scientists, science philosophers, and science educators have spent much effort defining science and describing how it happens, providing readers with insights into the nature of science (NOS). The nature of science focuses mainly on clarifying the character of scientific knowledge because science is essentially a knowledge-gathering enterprise. Examples of issues relevant to the nature of science include:

- How scientists generate research questions.
- How scientists inquire into science.
- How scientific knowledge is tested.
- How scientific knowledge changes.
- How scientific ideas are affected by social, cultural, and political contexts.

Considering ideas about the nature of science helps people construct more realistic views of science, helps guide the content and structure of science programs, and influences how science is taught. The sheer amount of this literature can be overwhelming, however; to make sense of it all we can start by looking at how science is defined in two major science education documents, the *Common Framework of Science Learning Outcomes* (Council of Ministers of Education, Canada, 1997) and *Science for All Americans* (Rutherford and Ahlgren, 1989). Contributors to these two documents worked to develop a consensus about the nature of science and outline what scientifically literate citizens need to know and be able to do. The following sections discuss these and other ideas. We ask you to think about how these ideas are similar to or different from your own ideas about science.

Science is about describing and explaining the natural world. Scientific inquiry is based on the assumption that the world is fundamentally understandable. Scientists aim to describe and explain the natural world, using a blend of imagination, observation, and logic. Science is based on the assumption that things and events in the natural world occur in consistent patterns that can be described and explained through careful, systematic observation and inquiry. Scientific descriptions and explanations are organized into a body of knowledge that consists of observations, measurements, concepts, laws, theories, and so on—the content or knowledge of science.

Science is a creative human activity, a product of human minds. Scientists' existing ideas influence what questions are asked, how those questions are studied, and how the results are interpreted. Before beginning a scientific research project in a particular area of knowledge, scientists spend much time thinking about what they know and do not know about that area. They design the research project to answer carefully selected questions, in order to further their knowledge and develop deeper insights. But this process does not include any guarantees—scientists may assess their existing knowledge incorrectly, they may fail to ask the right questions, their research design may be faulty, the research may fail to generate meaningful results, or they may interpret the results in the wrong way. Scientists are people as well as professionals, and no matter how carefully and thoughtfully they plan and work, they can make mistakes, fail to consider crucial elements, and be led astray by their existing ideas and expectations. Thus, the ideas and explanations constructed by scientists at the conclusion of a project may or may not become part of valid scientific knowledge.

Science is constrained by the professional practice of scientists and the reality of the natural world. Science does not support the idea that any notion a scientist constructs is a good idea that then becomes part of scientific knowledge. Scientists' ideas are intensely scrutinized by colleagues, who may attempt to replicate the results of experiments or cast doubt on the assumptions behind the ideas. Science, then, is constrained by the professional practice of scientists and when faced with new, contradictory evidence, some scientists change their explanations.

Also, the natural world is what it is. Explanations that enjoy considerable support may be refuted by new observations. For example, once most scientists believed that the continents were always in their current locations. They gave little weight to the fact that continents appeared to have a common biological and geological history that then appeared to diverge and the fact that the east coast of South America looked like it once was joined to the west coast of Africa. But observations based on a new technology that can measure changing magnetic fields on ocean floors surrounding deep, active trenches convinced most scientists that the continents had once been connected and had since drifted apart. Science then, is constrained by the reality of the natural world and scientific ideas are tentative and subject to change.

Science is a value-laden social, cultural, and political enterprise. Science is a human endeavor strongly influenced by scientists' ideas and perceptions. But scientists' ideas and perceptions, in turn, are strongly influenced by the social, cultural, economic, and political contexts, which help shape people's values, beliefs, need for peer recognition and acceptance, personal biases, and many other personal characteristics. Thus, these contexts have a powerful effect on the kind of science that is done. For example, a society that values helping the weak more than it values national security will pursue different scientific research objectives than a society that values national security above all. Or, consider how various political parties currently view issues such as global warming, cloning, stem cell research, and weapons development. It is clear that, in controversial areas, research funding may be largely determined by political and economic realities—that is, politics and economics may determine which questions scientists can pursue. Thus, science is value-laden and is a social, cultural, and political enterprise.

(To think about how these ideas about the nature of science can be thought about in another context, go to the Companion Manual and do Textbook Activity 1.2.)

What do these brief descriptions of various aspects of the scientific enterprise mean for the elementary school science teacher? If these are authentic descriptions of how science happens, and if we want children to have an accurate view of science, then we have an obligation to use these truths to help direct how we teach science and how we talk about science with children. (To get a sense of what's involved in talking with children about science, go to the Companion Manual and do Textbook Activity 1.3.)

Why Teach Science?

Science has so long been part of school programs that we tend to accept its presence uncritically—our attitude says, "Of course science should be taught in schools," but it does not say why. We might well ask:

- How does teaching science benefit teachers?
- How does participating in classroom science experiences benefit children?

When we ask experienced elementary science teachers to talk about teaching science to children they describe the strong interest displayed by children as they work on topics such as plants, animals, rocks, and weather. The children's enthusiasm and their impulse to go beyond the lesson catalyze the teacher's own interest in science. Teachers also describe moments when a child is able to connect related scientific ideas while constructing an explanation for some phenomenon—perhaps one that had long puzzled the child—for instance, explaining why water forms on the outside of a cold can of pop. Such moments exemplify why teaching science is worthwhile: you know that you are making a difference in the lives of children and helping them translate their wonder and curiosity into a deeper understanding of the natural world. What is more, through your work with children, you get to see the world freshly through their eyes, to experience again the awe-inspiring world in which we live, and to grow in your own understanding of science.

Teaching children science can help them understand scientific knowledge and the nature and practice of science. Understanding science helps children understand the natural world and critique their own unscientific ideas (e.g., that cold pop cans leak water). Understanding science helps children develop thoughtful attitudes about science as a human activity and gives them insight into the status of scientific explanations. Children learn that scientific ideas can change—for instance, the idea that the sun revolves around the earth. And they learn how to do science by developing science inquiry skills. In other words, teaching children science helps them develop scientific literacy (see the next section).

(In your Companion Manual, Textbook Activity 1.4 asks you to consider this issue of "why teach science?" in relation to science teaching resources.)

What Is Scientific Literacy?

A scientifically literate person is one who has the knowledge, skills, and attitudes needed to construct informed opinions and make informed decisions about issues related to science, technology, and society. For example, some issues change over time (e.g., the degree to which we should depend on fossil fuels) and all citizens need to be willing to consider new information, critically analyze that information, and re-think previously held opinions – in other words, become lifelong learners.

Definitions of scientific literacy tend to contain two elements–a description of the required knowledge, skills, and attitudes and an explanation of how the knowledge, skills, and attitudes are used by a scientifically literate person. The knowledge needed for scientific literacy includes knowledge of science content as a connected and interrelated whole as opposed to isolated or disjointed facts. For example, knowing about the structure and function of living systems will involve connecting a range of interrelated ideas about cells, energy, organisms, and ecosystems. The skills and attitudes needed for scientific literacy include the ability and willingness to reason, think creatively, construct logical arguments, make decisions, and solve problems. Literate people use such knowledge, skills, and attitudes to:

- *Engage intelligently in public debates about issues related to science.* Scientifically literate people know the background scientific knowledge necessary for informed debate on such issues as global warming, cloning, stem cell research, and DNA–related technologies.

- *Participate in community decisions.* Scientifically literate people understand the nature and importance of issues such as recycling, urban sprawl, and water supply, and the trade-offs involved when taking action on these issues.

- *Experience the natural world with deep understanding.* Scientifically literate people understand ideas such as the interrelationships among ecosystems and explanations of weather extremes.

- *Distinguish between science and pseudo–science.* Scientifically literate people understand what science is and what kinds of claims can be made by science. They know how to think critically about the claim that the ancient Egyptians used engineering principles to build the pyramids versus the claim that aliens arrived on Earth and helped the Egyptians build the pyramids.

- *Correctly interpret popular reports of science.* Scientifically literate people can correctly assess science reports in newspapers and magazines. For example, if an article about the possibility that weather makes people sick cites unnamed scientists and undisclosed evidence, scientifically literate people would correctly assess the degree of uncertainty in the article's assertions.

- *Debate the limits of science and technology.* Scientifically literate people understand the social, cultural, and political nature of science. For example, they recognize the social, cultural, and political contexts of such questions as whether new technology can solve environmental problems.

- *Make personal decisions.* Scientifically literate people understand how personal decisions affect the environment and other people–for example, decisions about which household products to use and which vehicles to drive.

(In your Companion Manual, Textbook Activity 1.5 asks you to consider your own degree of and attitudes toward scientific literacy.)

Thinking About Technology
What is Technology?

When you answered the questions about technology at the beginning of this chapter, you may have been thinking especially about computers and the Internet–that is, about information technology. For the most part, however, discussions of technology in this textbook will be much broader in scope, as reflected by the following definition (Council of Ministers of Education, Canada, 1997; International Technology Education Association, 2000; Pacey, 1983):

> Technology is a creative human activity focused on wants and needs and is based on our desire to constantly improve our condition and adapt to the environment. Technology is focused on the manufactured world. Technology has a technical aspect (associated knowledge, skills and techniques; devices and products), an organizational aspect (related economic and industrial activity; professional activity), and a cultural aspect (reflects cultural goals and values of diverse societies over time).

By this definition, almost every object we use could be referred to as technology. For example, this textbook qualifies as technology because it was created to store information in an easily accessible form. The highlighter you might be using to mark this textbook is technology because it was created to help you study. The clothes you wear, the cup you drink from, the chair you sit on, and the computer you use are all examples of technology. They were all made to address some want or need–that is, they all have some purpose. Notice how this aspect of addressing a want or need, of having a purpose, reflects the values held by a society. For example, there would be no need for textbooks if we did not value storing information in easily accessible forms. To use the words of the definition above, "our desire to constantly improve our condition" is based on our values, which tell us what would constitute an improvement. This point has led many researchers to describe technology as value-laden (Pacey, 1983; Layton, 1993).

Now think for a moment about what it takes to design and manufacture purposeful products like these. First, people needed to be convinced that there truly was a need for such products and that there will likely be an economic payoff (these considerations reflect the cultural aspect of technology). Then, individuals are needed with a wide range of knowledge (e.g., in science and mathematics) and a wide range of skills (e.g., in planning, drawing, and communicating) to design such products (reflecting the technical aspect of technology). Finally, a company is generally needed to manufacture and distribute such products (the organizational aspect of technology).

The core of technology is design, the strategy by which new technologies are developed and improved. Design is an iterative problem-solving process characterized by the following steps that are repeated as often as necessary:

- The design team identifies a problem that focuses around a human need or want.
- The problem is researched and the team generates a number of possible solutions.
- The solutions are carefully considered in light of the original requirements and various constraints (e.g., physical laws, cost, materials, aesthetics).
- Eventually one design (or possibly more than one) is chosen as the one to pursue, and is modeled, tested, and revised.

To teach an authentic image of technology you need to first develop an understanding of the nature of technology (NOT). An authentic image of technology is a less contentious issue than an authentic image of science, mainly because technology focuses around tangible objects (e.g., tables, vehicles, airplanes) rather than abstract knowledge (e.g., laws and theories). Most of the debate over the nature of technology relates to the positive and negative effects of technology on our lives and society and can be summed up in two contrasting views:

- Technology is an inherently negative social force that misdirects our lives.
- Technology is an inherently positive social force but societies may choose to build certain technologies and to use them for negative purposes (e.g., nuclear energy can be used to make destructive bombs or to power industrial production).

When considering the nature of technology it is important to keep in mind that we do not mean just the objects of technology but technology as an enterprise or endeavor. To view technology as just objects is an incomplete notion, similar to viewing science as just a body of knowledge. A comprehensive view of technology should include the following:

- An understanding of the knowledge required to design and make technological objects and devices (e.g., understanding the technological and scientific concepts related to designing and building the object).
- The technological capability (e.g., skills and knowledge) needed to design and make technological objects.
- An understanding of how technology relates to science and society (e.g., why the product is needed and the societal values represented by those needs).
- An understanding of the designed world (e.g., industry related to the manufacture of technological objects).

(To get a better sense of the importance of a comprehensive view of technology, turn to your Companion Manual and do Textbook Activity 1.6.)

Why Teach Technology?

North American science standards make specific reference to the importance of students learning about both science and technology. The explicit inclusion of technology in science education is relatively new in North America, however it is not surprising since there are many reasons why teaching students about technology is important:

- *Technology is everywhere and our daily lives are even more directly affected by technology than by science (e.g., we drive automobiles, use kitchen appliances, and work on computers).* Even young children are daily exposed to technology, for example, bicycles, toys, and games are all technological products.

- *Technology education prepares students to analyze technology-related social issues.* For example, an understanding and awareness of the social and environmental consequences of technological acts such as building and driving cars.

- *Technology education provides opportunities for students to participate in solving authentic problems and provides a context in which students with a 'practical bent' can succeed.* For example, a context in which students with superior manipulative, spatial, and problem-solving skills can excel.

- *Technology education helps students develop the knowledge, skills, and attitudes required for participation in a technological world.* For example, skills involved in assembling, dismantling, and repairing technological objects.

The knowledge, skills, and attitudes related to technological design are developed in the context of active investigation. The primary instructional strategy is technological problem solving, with design at its core. Technological problem solving is to technology teaching as scientific inquiry is to science teaching (see Chapter 3 for a more in-depth discussion of how scientific inquiry and technological problem-solving are defined). Students develop the abilities of technological problem-solving by actively solving and reflecting on design problems. The primary goal of technology teaching, however, is to help students develop technological literacy.

What Is Technological Literacy?

In a general way, the concept of technological literacy resembles that of scientific literacy–for example, the reasons for understanding technology are similar to the reasons for understanding science, particularly with respect to the ability to make informed decisions. However, at a specific level the two concepts are somewhat different, in that technological literacy focuses on a person's ability to understand "in increasingly sophisticated ways that evolve over time, what technology is, how it is created, and how it shapes society, and in turn is shaped by society" (International Technology Education Association [ITEA], 2000, p. 9). Nevertheless, many of the crucial issues that face our society (e.g., ensuring freshwater supplies and decreasing our dependence on fossil fuels) demand solutions that are informed by both science and technology–that is, they require decisions by people who are both scientifically and technologically literate. Recognition of the interdependency of science and technology has led some researchers to argue "this interdependency should inform 'authentic' science education and technology education" (Gilbert, Boulter, and Elmer, 2000, p. 8).

According to the ITEA standards, technologically literate people should be able to:

- *Evaluate and form opinions on technology reports presented in the media.* For example, evaluate the degree to which the technology represents a viable solution to a human need.

- *Better assess products and make more intelligent buying decisions.* For example, deciding whether to use cloth or disposable diapers for their children.

- *Make better societal decisions.* For example, decide whether society should reduce carbon dioxide emissions in an attempt to slow down global warming.

In order to begin to develop technological literacy, students need to develop an interrelated set of knowledge, skills, and attitudes:

- *Knowledge about the nature of technology* (e.g., an understanding of the scope of technology, how it changes, and how it relates to science and society).

- *Knowledge about technological concepts* (e.g., an understanding of important ideas used to design and build technological products).

- *Understanding of the societal aspects of technological problem solving* (e.g., an understanding of the cultural, social, economic, and political influence of technology).

- *Technological problem-solving skills* (e.g., skills involved in identifying a need, designing possible solutions, and assessing the impact of products).

- *Understanding of the designed world* (e.g., understanding related economic and industrial activity).

In this textbook, we acknowledge the importance of helping students develop scientific and technological literacy and believe that engaging children in scientific inquiry, technological problem-solving, and STS decision-making supports the attainment of these goals (see Chapter 3 for how these terms are defined).

Thinking About Connections Between Science and Technology

Science and technology have been portrayed here as sharing some attributes (e.g., both are influenced by society) and being unlike in other ways (e.g., a focus on the natural world versus a focus on the manufactured world). Figure 1.1 summarizes these and other similarities and differences between science and technology.

Figure 1.1
Similarities and Differences Between Science and Technology

Science	Technology
Focused on the natural world.	Focused on the manufactured world.
Investigations arise from human curiosity about the natural world.	Investigations arise from human needs and wants.
Concerned with constructing explanations (Why?).	Concerned with constructing workable products (How?).
Investigative approach is scientific inquiry.	Investigative approach is technological problem solving.
Centers around the interplay of evidence and explanation.	Centers around the interplay of designing and making.
Theoretical activity.	Practical activity.
Little or no design.	Design is a key feature.
Evaluation involves asking 'Does the explanation fit the evidence?'	Evaluation involves asking 'Is the product cost efficient? Does is work? What are the risks and benefits? Does the product stand up to repeated use?'

Science and Technology
Human pursuits.
Involve collaborating with others, constructing ideas, generating alternatives, and representing ideas.
Value-laden and influenced by society.
Change over time.
Involve knowledge, skills, and attitudes.

What is the Relationship Between Science and Technology?

At the beginning of this chapter you read that simply viewing technology as applied science was an oversimplification and historically inaccurate. Yet it remains that when many pre-service teachers are asked to describe the relationship between science and technology, they answer that scientific ideas give rise to technological ideas (S gives rise to T). If you read the history of scientific and technological ideas and how they came to be, you can certainly find some examples to support this view:

- The electric motor is based on the law of magnetism that like poles of magnets repel each other, as well as the principle that an electrical current travels in a single direction.

- The duplicating technique of the photocopier is based on the discovery that a certain type of material acts as a conductor in the light and an insulator in the dark. The photocopier is also based on the law of electrostatics that unlike charges attract.

- The creation of the atomic bomb was based on the discovery that when the nucleus of a heavy element such as uranium absorbs a neutron a tremendous amount of energy is generated.

Unfortunately, a belief in this view of the relationship between science and technology casts science in a gate keeping role – first you must know the science, then you can use these ideas to build the technology. Technology is portrayed as an offshoot of science that somehow seems less valued than science.

Historical study, however, also reveals that technological innovation may precede and provoke the development of scientific knowledge (T gives rise to S). If anything, it could be argued that a great deal of technology was developed long before science came into being and that technology has historical precedence over science. Particularly in regard to older technologies, the underlying science was clarified after the fact (sometimes long after) rather than used as a basis from which to develop technology. For example:

- The six simple machines: lever, wheel and axle, pulley, inclined plane, wedge, and screw were created in ancient times, without understanding of mechanical advantage.

- Gunpowder was developed and used in ancient China but the mechanisms of combustion and oxidation reactions were not understood until the 18th century.

- For centuries, indigenous peoples in North America made and applied a paste of moldy corn to prevent the infection of wounds. However, bacteria were first seen through a microscope in the 17th century, the germ theory of disease was introduced in 1864, and how antibiotics worked was not understood until the 20th century.

Historical examples such as those listed above have led some people to expand their view of the relationship between science and technology. In this view, people believe that science can give rise to technology and technology can give rise to science. This view puts science and technology on an equal footing and is more historically accurate. Science and technology are seen as different, but equal.

A final way of looking at the relationship between science and technology involves society (STS). This view acknowledges that while some science gave rise to technology, in other instances technology preceded the understanding of related science concepts. Regardless, society was inextricably linked to all scientific and technological endeavors in that these endeavors reflected the needs and wants of diverse societies. Rather than just dealing with the interplay between science and technology, STS considers the many complex interactions among science, technology, and society (and environment). For example, an STS view recognizes that:

- New scientific discoveries can inform current and new technology (e.g., the laser and research on light).

- New technology can assist scientific inquiry and the generation of new scientific discoveries (e.g., the electron microscope).

- Society influences the kinds of scientific questions that are asked (e.g., questions about stem cell research) and the kinds of technology that are built (e.g., technology that allows us to harvest stem cells).

- Technology that is created (e.g., the automobile) and scientific ideas that are constructed (e.g., the science behind organ transplants) influence the direction of society.

One way for you to understand what is meant by an STS approach to teaching is to compare the kinds of questions that are linked to scientific inquiry, technological problem solving, and STS decision-making. Each focuses around different kinds of questions:

- Scientific inquiry: Why?
- Technological problem solving: How?
- STS decision-making: Should?

Table 1.1 shows comparisons between questions that underpin scientific inquiry, technological problem solving, and STS decision-making.

(To get a sense of the images of science and technology in the Alberta Elementary Science Program, go to the Companion Manual and do Textbook Activity 1.7.)

Thinking About Implications for the Classroom

The *Common Framework of Science Learning Outcomes* (CMEC, 1997) recognizes a clear connection between science and technology in Foundation Statement One. Within this foundation statement, students are directed to develop an understanding of the relationship between science and technology, how they interact, and how they develop within a social context. For example, in the elementary science classroom children can develop

scientific understanding of electricity (the natural world), by inquiring into how differently configured electric circuits work or don't work. They can then apply that knowledge and use their problem-solving abilities to build a circuit of Christmas-tree lights that won't fail when a single bulb fails (the manufactured world). This type of process helps children see some of the similarities and differences between science and technology. Both the inquiry into electricity and problem-solving efforts to design Christmas tree lights reflect our societal context. Our society values inquiry into science that can change our world for the better and for the most part, values innovations that allow us to enhance our experiences of holiday traditions.

The Council of Ministers of Education, Canada (1997) and Rutherford and Ahlgren (1989) provide information about what schools can do to help students develop scientific and technological literacy. They advise that:

- *Schools need to help students develop knowledge, skills, and attitudes.* Students who develop these proficiencies will be able to develop technological problem solving, scientific inquiry, and STS decision-making abilities.

- *Schools need to emphasize and explain the dependency of living things on each other and on the environment.* Students who understand the interdependency of living things and the environment will develop an intelligent respect for nature that should inform their decisions about how to live.

Table 1.1

Questions for Scientific Inquiry, Technological Problem-Solving, and STS Decision–Making

Scientific Inquiry	Technological Problem-Solving	STS Decision-Making
Why?	How?	Should?
Why does petroleum form inside the Earth?	How is motor oil manufactured from crude petroleum?	Should used motor oil be recycled?
Why does the moon have phases?	How can we examine the moon more closely?	Should we spend money traveling to the moon?
What factors affect the intensity of earthquakes?	How can we measure the strength of an earthquake?	Should we build structures within known earthquake zones?

- *Schools need to help students understand the interrelationships between science, technology, and society.* Students who understand the inevitable side effects of science and technology on the environment, and the social and environmental contexts of science and technology, will likely move beyond considering their own self-interest to a more global perspective that will affect their careers, personal lives, and their futures.

Summary Ideas

This chapter provides definitions for science and technology and discusses the role that science and technology education plays in supporting the development of scientific and technological literacy. The chapter presents some current thinking about:

- *How science and technology are defined.* Science is focused on describing and explaining the natural world. Scientific inquiry refers to the ways in which scientific knowledge is constructed and justified. Technology is focused on the manufactured world and is based on our desire to constantly improve our condition and adapt to the environment. The primary instructional strategy for technology is technological problem solving, with design at its core. Technological problem solving is to technology teaching as scientific inquiry is to science teaching.

- *Why we should teach science and technology.* Teaching children science can help them to understand scientific knowledge, and the nature and practice of science. Teaching children technology helps them understand the technical, organizational, and cultural aspects of manufactured objects. The overall reason for teaching science and technology is to develop scientifically and technologically literate people who can make informed decisions about important social issues.

- **Differences and similarities between science and technology.** Both science and technology are value laden, human pursuits that change over time and are based on a foundation of knowledge and skills. While science and technology are connected, they are also different in important ways.

- **Relationships between science and technology.** Science ideas can give rise to technology. Technology can give rise to science. Both science and technology are influenced by society's needs and wants and in turn can influence the direction of a society.

- *Science, technology, and society.* Science and technology need to be looked at in a social context because science and technology affect society and society affects science

and technology. STS is a teaching context that allows for the examination of the interconnection between science, technology, and society.

- *How we should teach STS.* Scientific inquiry and technological problem solving are two instructional strategies used to teach about the contexts of science and technology. An instructional strategy used to teach about the context of STS is called STS decision-making and involves investigating and deciding on courses of action in relation to science and technology-related social issues.

Making Productive Connections

Scenario

You have just been hired as an elementary teacher. The principal asks you to prepare a list of general learning goals for your children for the coming year. What would be your goals for science? How do your goals relate to what you read in Chapter 1?

Report

In the Common Framework of Science Learning Outcomes (CMEC, 1997), authors write that science education:

> Will be a key element in developing scientific literacy and in building a strong future for Canada's young people. (p. 5)

What do you think an elementary science teacher can do to contribute to these goals? Do you agree that these should be the goals of education? Why or why not?

Articles

Find three articles from newspapers or magazines that describe examples of current science and technology-related social issues that personally interest you. Then answer the following questions:

- What are some scientific inquiry questions related to your issues?

- What are some technological problem-solving questions related to your issues?

- What are some STS decision-making questions related to your issues?

Ideas to Think About When Teaching Science, Technology, and Society

- Why am I teaching science (or technology) in the ways that I am?

- What do the ways I teach science imply about my beliefs about science and science teaching?

- What do the ways I teach technology imply about my beliefs about technology and technology teaching?

- What do the ways I teach science convey to my students about science, technology and society?

- Why have I selected the teaching resources that I use on a daily basis?

- How do other teachers I know teach science?

- How are their ways of teaching the same as and different from my ways? Why do our practices differ?

Selected Readings

Bybee, R. W. (1997). *Achieving Scientific Literacy: From Purposes to Practices.* Portsmouth, N.H.: Heinemann.

The author examines educational reform since World War II, introduces different points of view about scientific literacy, and provides suggestions for designing school science programs.

Council of Ministers of Education, Canada (1997). *Common Framework of Science Learning Outcomes.* Council of Ministers of Education, Canada: ON.

Authors outline a vision of scientific literacy that includes science-related knowledge, skills, and attitudes that enable the analysis of interrelationships among science, technology, and society (STS).

International Technology Education Association (2000). *Standards for Technological Literacy: Content for the Study of Technology.* Reston, Va.: ITEA.

The ITEA standards document outlines ideas about how to prepare children for a technological world; it can be used to enrich children's technology experiences through its many links to the *NSE Standards.*

National Research Council (1996). *National Science Education Standards.* Washington, D.C.: National Academy Press.

This is the *NSE Standards* (American) document that is referred to in this textbook.

Roberts, D. A. (1982). Developing the concept of "curriculum emphases" in science education. *Science Education*, 66(2), 243-260.

This important article describes how different science programs contain different messages about why teachers should be teaching science to children. The author provides a useful framework for analyzing school science programs.

Selected Websites

COMMON FRAMEWORK OF SCIENCE LEARNING OUTCOMES
http://www.CMEC.CA/science/framework
This website contains an online version of the Canadian science learning outcomes.

NORTH CAROLINA STATE UNIVERSITY: SCIENCE, TECHNOLOGY, AND SOCIETY
http://www.ncsu.edu/chass/mds/stslinks.html
This site provides a myriad of links related to science, technology, and society.

NATIONAL SCIENCE EDUCATION STANDARDS (NRC)
http://www.nap.edu/readingroom/books/nses/html
This website provides access to the NSE Standards document online.

INTERNATIONAL TECHNOLOGY EDUCATION ASSOCIATION (ITEA)
http://www.iteawww.org
The ITEA website defines technology and provides information about ITEA standards, conferences, publications and resources, and professional development.

UNIVERSITY OF ALBERTA: SCIENCE, TECHNOLOGY, AND SOCIETY
http://www.ualberta.ca/~slis/guides/scitech/kmc.htm
This website includes many links to sites related to science, technology, and society.

Chapter 2
Children's Learning in STS

Learning Objectives

In this chapter, you should learn

- Key ideas about learning that relate to scientific inquiry, technological problem solving, and STS decision-making.
- The importance of language experiences to scientific inquiry, technological problem solving, and STS decision-making.
- The meaning and significance of constructivist and social constructivist theories of learning.
- What our current ideas about learning imply for classroom teaching.

Thinking About Your Existing Ideas

Write down your answers to the following questions. After you complete this chapter, revisit your answers. Which of your ideas remained the same and which changed? How did they change, and what do you believe caused the changes?

- How do children learn?
- How can I teach so children will learn with understanding rather than memorize?
- How do I know if children are learning scientific inquiry, technological problem solving, and STS decision-making?
- What role do children's existing ideas play in future learning?
- How do ideas change?
- What roles do other people play in learning?
- What are the roles of talking, writing, reading, and drawing in scientific inquiry, technological problem solving, and STS decision-making?
- If students already have their own ideas that make sense to them, how can we bring them closer to an understanding of scientific inquiry, technological problem solving, and STS decision-making?

How Do Children Learn?

When you teach, your teaching strategies will be based on your current ideas about how children learn, on your own personal theory of learning. Your learning theory will be more implicit than explicit and somewhat loosely structured. For example, your theory might include that children learn best when they collaborate so your lessons will incorporate opportunities for them to work together in small groups. Or your learning theory could include that children need to explore ideas using concrete materials so you will incorporate activities where children manipulate materials into your lessons.

Your ideas about how children learn will also have implications for other important aspects of your teaching such as lesson planning, assessment, and resource selection. For example, if you believe that *how* students do science is as important as *what* they find out, you will include opportunities for them to predict, observe, experiment, and explain. If you believe that students' learning should be assessed in ways that correspond to how they are taught, you may decide to use performance assessments that involve scientific inquiry tasks. If you believe that children need to connect their classroom learning with the world around them you will base lessons on support resources that help them do this.

You may think that your theory of learning is unimportant and that all that counts is what you to do in the classroom. But all classroom practice is driven by some implicit or explicit theory; there is no divide between theory and practice. Consciously or not, as you teach, you base what you do on your beliefs about learning. As a prospective teacher, then, you need to reflect on both your own personal theory of learning and the theories of learning developed by educators and researchers. This will help you to refine and develop your understanding of learning and improve your teaching practice.

The Importance of Understanding

Understanding is the primary goal of learning, and has to do with relating ideas to each other and seeing how they fit together. Implicit in the notion of understanding is the sense of an integrated whole, of the big picture rather than bits and pieces. Many of us have had 'aha' types of experiences where what was previously a haphazard collection of fragments seemed to suddenly come together and make sense to us. Teachers often perceive the same type of event in their classrooms, when children light up and seem to exclaim, "Now I get it!"

Understanding, then, is the comprehension of a totality or an integrated whole, a grasp of both the elements of what is being learned and the connections and interactions among those elements. Understanding involves a significant change in an entire set of ideas rather than just the simple addition of another piece of knowledge. For example, knowing why some birds fly south for the winter involves understanding, while knowing that ravens are black requires only the awareness of a particular fact.

Understanding and explaining are linked. We generally assume that those who understand can explain to others and the ability to explain something is taken as an indication that the explainer does understand. For example, a clear explanation of why a whale is a mammal and not a fish is evidence that the explainer understands characteristics of mammals. Or, an accurate explanation of why a triangle is a strong building shape is evidence that the explainer understands certain engineering principles. Of course, such explanations should be in the explainer's own words and be based on connections generated by the learner rather than connections provided by the teacher.

The ability to properly transfer learning to a new situation is considered strong evidence of understanding. For example, when a student takes a classification system for minerals and accurately applies it to a new set of minerals, then this is considered to indicate understanding of the classification system. Or, when a student realizes why a clay ball sinks and a clay boat made of the same clay floats, then applies that understanding to explain why raisins bob up and down in soda pop, this is considered to indicate that the student understands some key principles of buoyancy.

Learning and Evidence of Understanding

As a teacher, you quickly become familiar with the idea that students need to meet behavioral objectives. Behavioral objectives are stated in "will" or "will be able to" language and include an action verb such as "state" or "construct". Examples of behavioral objectives are:

- Scientific inquiry: "Students will be able to state three examples of mammals."
- Technological problem-solving: "Students will be able to construct a bridge using 50 paper straws that spans a 50 cm gap and supports a 100 g weight."
- STS decision-making: "Students will be able to provide two scientific reasons to support their decision as to what action should be taken about fossil fuel emissions."

You need to keep in mind that behavioral objectives always imply questions about underlying mental activity, e.g., "What thinking underlies a student's ability to state three examples of mammals? Does the student need to know the definition or characteristics of a mammal?" Or, "What scientific or technological ideas does a student need to grasp in order to be able to build the required bridge? Does the student need to realize that a triangle is a strong shape?" By focusing solely on behavioral objectives you risk not noticing that students may meet those objectives in an unthinking manner. For example, students may memorize the definition of "condensation" without comprehending the role condensation plays in the water cycle. You must also pay attention to the changes in thinking that need to occur if the required behavior is to be mastered with understanding.

Learning involves changes in thinking and understanding is the overall goal of teaching but there still remains the practical need for teachers to gather observable evidence that learning has taken place. Thus it is helpful for you to keep in mind the importance of both learning and evidence of learning. We cannot see the changes in student thinking (i.e., changes that we assume are taking place in their brains as a result of teaching) so this is where behavioral objectives play their role. Student behaviors such as talking, writing, and demonstrating provide us with useful clues as to how their thinking has changed.

Theories of Learning

Researchers and educators have developed different theories to try to explain how learning takes place. Theories differ in terms of their guiding concepts, view of knowledge, view of teaching, and view of the learner, as well as in other significant ways. The discipline of psychology–the study of behavior and mental processes–has been the main source of theories of learning in education. Other ideas have come from studies of philosophy, language, social groups, human behavior, the brain, and artificial intelligence.

Not surprisingly, theories of learning have changed over the years and current beliefs about learning differ from those held in previous eras. Theory changes have occurred both in education generally and in specific subject areas such as science and technology. Major influences on ideas about learning include both factors within education (e.g., findings from research studies) and factors outside education (e.g., developments in other fields of study such as artificial intelligence).

Behaviorism and Cognitivism

Educators have traditionally defined learning in two quite different ways, from a behaviorist perspective and from a cognitivist perspective. Both equate learning with change but behaviorist theory focuses on changes in what children can *do* while cognitivist theory focuses on changes in what children *know*. From the behaviorist perspective, learning means that the learner can now *do* something that he or she could not do before. From the cognitivist perspective, learning means that the learner now *knows* something that she or he did not know before. In education, there has been a gradual shift in emphasis from behaviorist to cognitivist theories.

Behaviorist Learning Theory

Behaviorist learning theory originated in the early 20th century and held sway in psychology and education through the 1920s, 30s, and 40s. The founders of behaviorism studied observable behaviour and considered that what went on inside the brain or mind of the learner could not be seen and hence was not an appropriate subject of study. Some later behaviorists paid more attention to mental events but behavior remained their main focus.

The fundamental idea underlying behaviourism is stimulus-response (S-R) conditioning. *Conditioning* refers to the shaping of behavior by rewards and punishments. In S-R conditioning, subjects are repeatedly exposed to a stimulus that aims at eliciting a specific behavioural response. Subjects are rewarded for the desired response or punished for other responses. If conditioning is successful, their behavior is eventually shaped so that only the desired response occurs. For example, the subjects could be students, the stimulus could be a lesson on using a microscope, the desired response could be correctly using the microscope, and the reward for success could be a grade of A+.

Although behaviourism no longer dominates education, it still plays an important role. For example:

- Teachers use behavioral evidence to get feedback about the effects of their teaching. The behavioral evidence is often framed as a learning objective along the lines of, "Students will be able to A," where A denotes an action such as explain, draw, demonstrate, or build.

- Teachers use rewards and punishments to reinforce desirable student behaviors (e.g. complimenting students when they contribute to classroom discussion).

- Students use repeated practice to perfect a skill (e.g., students practice reading volumes on a graduated cylinder to become more adept at making correct measurements of liquid volume).

The main criticism of behaviourism is that human behavior has to be looked at as purposive or intelligent (i.e., that behavior results from mental activities) and that behaviorism fails to account for the thinking that must underlie behavior. Another criticism is that psychological/behavioral events can be understood only if looked at as organized wholes rather than being broken down into small pieces such as stimulus-response units.

Cognitivist Learning Theory

Cognitivism, a relatively new area of psychology focusing on *how people think*, started to gain influence in the 1950s, then gathered impetus through the 1960s. With the rise of cognitivism, mental processes became an important topic of study. In cognitivist theories, learning is seen not as mere conditioning but as the development of understanding. Thinking is no longer viewed as just a response to a stimulus but as an interpretative process that develops or changes understanding. Constructivism, the dominant theory of learning in science education today, is a cognitive theory of learning because it focuses on the mental construction of ideas.

The basic unit of human knowledge in cognitivism is an idea or mental construct that defines or characterizes something and is denoted by a single word (e.g., *tree*), or a brief phrase (e.g., *mechanical advantage*). Each construct has defining attributes or properties that differentiates it from other constructs. Learning is considered a mental process involving the organization of individual constructs into increasingly complex relationships referred to as schemas or schemata. Schema theory, or the study of schemata, has very significant implications for thinking about learning:

- Learners are not blank slates but have existing networks of ideas, which influence new learning and which must be taken into account.

- Existing ideas influence the way learners view reality, whether as a child, an adult, a scientist, or a technologist.

- To build stable, meaningful networks of ideas (schemata), learners need learning opportunities that involve multiple interactions and experiences with appropriate objects or events. A single experience is unlikely to be sufficient to do more than give rise to a few, isolated ideas.

- If learning involves building complex networks of related ideas then it is important to both help children learn new ideas and to help them make connections among the ideas they are learning.

Learning Theory Applied to STS Education

Behaviorist and cognitivist learning theories have been widely applied to science education and have found their way into technology education. Major theorists whose ideas have been applied in these areas are Jean Piaget, Robert Gagne, Jerome Bruner, David Ausubel, and Lev Vygotsky. Their most important contributions are summarized in Table 2.1.

Jean Piaget

Jean Piaget studied the *developmental stages* of children as they related to the kind of knowledge they can acquire at each stage, so his theories have more to do with children's readiness for learning than with how their learning occurs. Strictly speaking, Piaget was not a learning theorist, but his basic ideas have been so widely discussed in relation to learning theory that it is necessary to mention him here.

Piaget suggests that all children go through a hierarchy of four developmental stages loosely tied to age ranges that need to be taken into account when considering what they may be capable of learning at a particular age. Piaget calls these four stages *sensorimotor, pre-operational, concrete operational, and formal operational* (see Table 2.2).

Critics of Piaget's stage theory have suggested that the stages are not as separate from each other as he implies but that they overlap. For example, researchers and teachers can provide examples of children in the concrete operational stage (7-11 years) who apparently contradict Piaget's idea that such children have little ability to conceptualize and think logically. Piaget's experimental methods have also been criticized on the grounds that his tasks were too difficult for the children he worked with

Table 2.1

Key Contributors in the Application of Learning Theories to Science Education

Learning Theorist	Theoretical Perspective	Three Important Ideas About Learning Science
Jean Piaget **(1896-1980)**	Developmentalism, cognitivism	• What children can learn depends in part on their age and level of development. • Children hold conceptions of natural phenomena that differ from scientists' ideas. • New ideas may be integrated with networks of previous ideas or may give rise to new networks of ideas.
Robert Gagne **(1916-2002)**	Behaviorism	• Science learning should include learning about scientific processes (i.e., the skills used by scientists) • Effective learning is a progression from simple to difficult. • Complex learning tasks should be broken down into simpler steps.
Jerome Bruner **(born 1915)**	Cognitivism, developmentalism	• Children are always ready to learn at some level. • Children should be actively involved in their learning. • Learning is more meaningful when children discover ideas for themselves.
David Ausubel **(born 1918)**	Cognitivism	• The most important single factor influencing learning is what the learner already knows. • Both reception and discovery learning can be meaningful. • Big ideas are important advance organizers for new learning
Lev Vygotsky **(1896-1934)**	Cognitivism	• Learning is influenced by language and social interaction. • Peers and instructors play important roles in learning. • Learning is most effective within a certain zone between the teacher's knowledge and the learner's capabilities.

which led him to underrate their true abilities relative to their ages. Other researchers have criticized Piaget for generalizing his ideas about children's abilities after working with only a few children, usually his own!

Piaget views knowledge as existing in the 'mind' in the form of mental structures or *schemata*, as fluid networks of related ideas that either persist or adapt and change. New knowledge is created and changed through a person's interaction with the environment via three related processes called *assimilation, equilibration,* and *accommodation.* Piaget claims that the driving force behind knowledge change is the person's need to maintain or achieve a state of *equilibrium* or balance with its surrounding environment. Piaget refers to this as the need to achieve the 'accord of thought with things'.

Knowledge change begins with the child attending to new information arriving from the environment. First, the child uses his or her existing schemata to *assimilate* (take in) the new information. Disequilibrium (unbalance with the environment) results when the new information does not fit and cannot be transformed to fit into already existing schemata. To return to a state of equilibration with the environment, the existing schemata must instead change in order to *accommodate* the new information. Generally only one schema needs to change but then the newly accommodated structure must also be reorganized to fit with other schemata. Piaget calls this entire process the 'accord of thought with thought' (see Figure 2.1).

Piaget's ideas had a powerful influence on science education. One of the three leading science programs of the 1960s, *Science Curriculum Improvement Study* or *SCIS* (Karplus & Thier, 1967), is based on Piagetian theory. SCIS suggests that pupils learn science through a 'Learning Cycle' of three stages or steps: exploration (of things), concept invention, and concept application.

Table 2.2

Piaget's Developmental Stages

Stage	Age Range	Characteristics
Sensorimotor	Infancy, 0-2 years	The infant progresses from simple uncoordinated reflexes (like sucking) to relatively organized sensorimotor actions in relation to the immediate environment.
Preoperational	Early childhood, 2-7 years	Representational thought begins. The child engages with the world of symbols and articulates thought through speech.
Concrete Operational	Middle childhood, 7-11 years	The child becomes rational, developing a coherent and integrated conceptual framework to bring systematically to bear on the surrounding world.
Formal Operational	Adolescence, 11-15 years	The child becomes capable of abstract, logical thought. The child can deal both with the immediate world and with the 'what if' world of possibility

These three stages are equivalent, respectively, to assimilation, disequilibrium/accommodation, and (new) equilibrium. (The importance of the 'Learning Cycle' model is described in more detail later in this chapter.)

Robert Gagne

The behaviorist Robert Gagne began working in the area of learning theory after training pilots during World War II. Gagne sees learning as a process of behaviour modification based on stimulus-response conditioning. When the learner is able to reproduce an observable response again and again, learning has occurred because the learner has acquired a new capability.

Gagne's basic approach to understanding learning involves constructing taxonomies that break major ideas about learning into hierarchical sets. For example, Gagne recognizes eight varieties of learning (signal, stimulus-response, chaining, verbal association, multiple discrimination, concept, principle, and problem-solving). He divides the act of learning into eight phases (motivation, apprehending, acquisition, retention, recall, generalization, performance, and feedback). He recognizes five types of learning outcomes or capabilities (verbal information, intellectual skills, cognitive strategies, attitudes, and motor skills). The common practice of categorizing learning goals into knowledge, skills, and attitudes (KSAs) has its roots in Gagne's five categories of learning outcomes.

Gagne's ideas guided the development of the *Science: A Process Approach* or *SAPA* program (American Association for the Advancement of Science, 1964). SAPA was highly structured, and the teacher carefully controlled the sequence of lessons. *SAPA*'s goal was for children to learn the 'processes of science' rather than science content or ideas. The program was built around Gagne's notion that science learning must include use of a set of generalizable principles for doing all science that he called *process skills*. Identified process skills included observing, classifying, measuring, predicting, controlling variables, and interpreting data. (Chapter 3 discusses skills in more detail and challenges some common myths about them.)

Jerome Bruner

Jerome Bruner, a professor of psychology at Harvard University and later at Oxford University, played a key role in bringing cognitivism into educational learning theory. In the 1940s, Bruner began studying how people's existing ideas influence their perceptions of the world, a notion similar to Piaget's schemata. Bruner also became interested in how human beings go about building a model of the world of their experience 'in their heads', and how human cognitive abilities develop in general. This led him to the study of children's cognitive development.

In 1959, Bruner chaired a ten-day meeting of leading U.S. scholars and educators to examine the implications of cognitivism for educational practice. One immediate result was his co-founding of the Harvard Center for Cognitive Studies. Another was the publication of his book, *The Process of Education* (1962), which

Figure 2.1
Piaget: The Accord of Thought with Thought

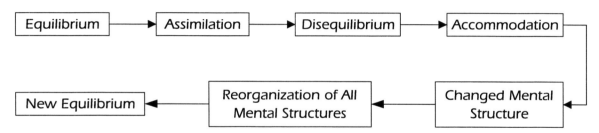

presented a powerful new image of the learner as an active, intuitive, intrinsically motivated problem-solver more than ready to wrestle with the challenges of learning. This contrasted sharply with behaviorism's image of a passive respondent to a stimulus and the Piagetian notion of a learner restricted by age-related stage development.

Like Piaget, Bruner thinks that developing human beings pass through stages of cognitive development but Bruner believes these stages are non-restrictive. Thus he asserts that the child is always ready to learn at some level–"Any subject can be taught effectively in some intellectually honest form to any child at any stage of development" (Bruner, 1962, p. 33). Bruner sees education as a process of knowledge gathering, and his main emphasis is on the process of learning (e.g., classifying clouds by their shapes) rather than the product (e.g., knowing that stratus clouds are usually associated with stormy weather).

Bruner views learning as an inductive process in the main, going from particular examples to general conclusions. The learner actively relates new knowledge to previous cognitive structures that represent a constructed model of reality that is the learner's view of how the world works. The mental model originates from the social context and is modified in light of subsequent experience (Bruner, 1962, 1962a, 1966). Learning involves three main phases—acquiring knowledge, transforming or going beyond the knowledge to adapt it to a purpose, and checking to ensure that the knowledge suits the purpose. Newly acquired knowledge may either fit with or contradict previous knowledge, adapting to or altering the learner's mental model of the world.

Bruner's ideas greatly influenced the design of the *Elementary Science Study* or *ESS* program (Education Development Center, 1960), which featured a student-centered approach and downplayed teacher intervention. *ESS* units consisted of a brief teacher guide and a kit of materials, and provided a lot of freedom for students to investigate their own questions. *ESS* emphasized Bruner's notion of learning as discovery and played a major role in popularizing the *discovery* approach to science. A discovery approach is based on the belief that given concrete materials and asked open-ended questions, children can discern the correct scientific explanations behind natural phenomena. Bruner proposed three main benefits of discovery learning–learning is done for intrinsic reasons, students

learn how to inquire and problem-solve (how to learn), and students can better recall what they learn.

David Ausubel

David Ausubel is a cognitive psychologist who came to education from the field of medicine where he studied the human brain. Ausubel's ideas about learning are laid out in detail in *Educational Psychology: A Cognitive View* (1968). Ausubel's book emphasizes the practicality of his ideas and he states that his main goal is to provide guidance for classroom teaching. His focus is on the fundamentals of classroom learning, which he refers to as 'meaningful symbolic learning' (i.e., learning centered around the meanings of words and what they represent). Ausubel categorizes classroom learning by making two separate distinctions:

- Reception learning versus discovery learning.
- Rote learning vs. meaningful learning.

Reception learning occurs when knowledge is presented to the student in final form (e.g., through a teacher explanation), while discovery learning occurs when the learner discovers knowledge through active investigation. Meaningful learning is related meaningfully to previous knowledge while rote learning is related arbitrarily to previous knowledge (memorization is a similar idea to rote learning.)

Ausubel questions Bruner's claim that discovery learning is superior to reception learning by arguing that either reception or discovery learning can be rote or meaningful, depending on how knowledge is presented to the learner. Direct teaching can still be meaningful to the student and does not have to result in rote learning. From the practical side, Ausubel notes that in a classroom some reception learning is always necessary because discovery learning is too time-consuming to be used all the time (and can also lead to children forming alternative conceptions).

Ausubel believes that learning occurs as a result of students' natural tendency to organize information into meaningful wholes. He proposes that reception learning can be made meaningful by first teaching students important general or big ideas called *advance organizers, which* provide an overarching framework into which they can fit the details of their new learning. Advance organizers must be carefully selected for relevance and inclusiveness so students can bridge the gap between what they already know and what they are about to learn. Using advance organizers to ensure meaningful learning requires three steps—presenting the advance organizers, moving from the advance organizers or general ideas to the specific details, and connecting the new and old ideas to make a coherent whole (Ausubel, 1968):

Ausubel is most famous for his statement that *the most important thing a child brings to learning is what he or she already knows.* Meaningful learning, then, occurs when new knowledge is consciously connected to existing knowledge in a useful way. The result is the modification and reorganization of the child's existing cognitive structures, similar to Piaget's notions of assimilation, equilibration, and accommodation. Ausubel's statement highlights his strong belief in the critical importance of taking into account students' existing ideas when teaching them something new.

Lev Vygotsky

Lev Vygotsky was a socio-cultural theorist who emphasized the roles of culture and society in learning. Vygotsky believed that children construct their own knowledge rather than receiving fully formed ideas from the teacher, but he also suggested that a child's cognitive constructions are socially mediated rather than purely individual. In other words, children's ideas about the world are influenced by their social interactions. Most significant are their interactions with adults such as teachers and parents and their interactions with their classroom peers.

Vygotsky places great importance on the role of language in both development and learning. He sees cognitive development as a matter of an individual's social interaction with others, mainly through language. As a child grows, words begin to take on meaning and the ability to communicate develops. Vygotsky sees language essentially as verbalized thought, as a medium both of inner thought and external speech. Thus, it is a key tool that children use to both plan and carry out learning tasks.

Vygotsky proposes that children's ideas can be divided into spontaneous and scientific conceptions. Spontaneous conceptions are unsystematic ideas that children develop mainly through their own experience and mental efforts, a notion somewhat similar to what modern-day constructivists call alternative conceptions. Scientific conceptions are formed by instruction through children's social interaction with teachers, parents, and other adults (Vygotsky, 1962, 1968). Vygotsky thought that spontaneous conceptions and scientific conceptions were both essential to the development of children's understanding.

Vygotsky views children's cognitive development as continuous rather than stage-like. While Piaget assumes that a child cannot learn until at the appropriate stage of development, Vygotsky assumes that learning precedes development, i.e., learning is the actual cause of the child's cognitive development and is like a locomotive that pulls the child ahead. Development is best fostered by learning that is just ahead of the child's current level of understanding so the key is to provide learning experiences that challenge students yet do not frustrate them (Vygotsky, 1962, 1968).

Important to Vygotsky's view of learning are his related ideas of the *zone of proximal development* (ZPD) and *scaffolding.* The ZPD is the distance between the actual developmental level of the child and the potential developmental level if the child were to learn in conjunction with adults or more capable peers. Adults and peers collaborate with and assist the child by *scaffolding*—explaining supplying information, questioning, correcting, and having the child explain (Vygotsky, 1962,1968). In science and technology education today, the ideas of Vygotsky are closely linked to what has come to be known as *social constructivism,* which focuses on how children construct their ideas about the world as they interact with other learners and with knowledgeable adults. The emphasis is on the social nature of learning rather than on individual learning.

Constructivism

Constructivism is a theory of learning with roots in the work of Piaget, Bruner, Ausubel, and Vygotsky. Today, constructivism is an important theory of learning in education generally and is currently the dominant theory in science and technology education. The key underlying assumption of constructivism is that *learners interpret what they are being taught in light of their existing ideas.* This contrasts with the more traditional view that learners simply receive and accept what they are taught in the form it is taught to them.

Constructivism focused initially on individual learning, an approach sometimes referred to as *cognitive constructivism,* and then further developed to take into account the social nature of learning, an approach commonly referred to as *social constructivism*. In this book, the term 'constructivism' will be used to collectively refer to both cognitive and social constructivism. Currently, the constructivist approach to learning has the most potential at this time to advance science and technology education because constructivism:

- Emphasizes the active participation of the learner in the development of ideas.

- Highlights the social nature of learning.

- Takes into account both the ideas of the learner and the currently accepted ideas.

- Has reinvigorated the discussion of science and technology learning by bringing out important issues related to knowledge in general and science and technology knowledge in particular.

In this book we will use constructivism as the general overall basis for our ideas about STS planning, teaching, and assessment.

Cognitive constructivism further develops cognitivist learning theory with a much increased emphasis on the existing ideas that the learner brings to learning. At the core of constructivism are the following four tenets:

- People construct their own understanding of the world, based on their own experiences.

- People's understanding of the world is organized into structures of related ideas called *schemata* that are then used to make sense of subsequent experiences.

- Learning is the process by which people modify old schemata or create new schemata in order to make sense of new experiences.

- It takes time to consider a new idea, compare it to existing ideas, and imaginatively restructure the new with the old.

The first premise means that children in classrooms will all have somewhat different understandings or interpretations of what you teach them. What is taught is not simply assimilated as is but is altered to varying degrees by each individual child. The second premise means that each child organizes what is learned into mental structures that influence how the child makes sense of subsequent learning. The child's mental structures act like filters for new learning and can be altered by new learning. The third premise means that learning is not just the simple accumulation of

information but is a complex process that can result in significant changes in how children view the world. The fourth premise means that children will only learn new ideas when they are given time to think about and wrestle with them, particularly if they are to learn them with any degree of understanding.

Drawing upon the ideas of Vygotsky, as well as other sociocultural theorists, *social constructivism* broadens the constructivist perspective by focusing on the social rather than the individual nature of learning. Social constructivists suggest that children's ideas are influenced by the social and cultural context within which their learning takes place, and see learning as a process of social development rather than as the development of individual cognitive schemes. In classrooms, the social context primarily involves interaction with teachers and peers, and the use of language in discussion, argument, and negotiation.

Following Vygotsky and his notion of a zone of proximal development, social constructivists suggest that teachers can best facilitate children's learning through social interaction by providing experiences just beyond children's current capability and assisting them to achieve the required new capability. This process of providing structured assistance is called scaffolding (see previous section on Lev Vygotsky).

Children's Alternative Conceptions

Because constructivists believe that children's existing ideas significantly affect how they make sense of what happens in science and technology classrooms, a major focus of constructivist research has been on identifying children's existing ideas about the natural world and, to a lesser extent, the manufactured world. Children of various ages have been interviewed in depth regarding their understanding of science and technology. Investigation into children's ideas is variously called *alternative conceptions research, alternative frameworks research, conceptual change research, and misconceptions research.*

Research into children's ideas suggests that:

- Children's existing ideas are comprised of both scientific and non-scientific ideas. Ideas that are different from scientists' ideas are referred to as *alternative conceptions*. For example, scientists attribute the change in the seasons mainly to the tilt of the earth's axis. In contrast, many children (and adults) believe seasonal change has to do with how close the earth is to the sun, even though in northern latitudes the earth is actually further from the sun in the summer than in the winter.

- Children's ideas are often strongly held and hard to change. Children may be reluctant to accept a new idea presented in class if it differs from their existing ideas. Even a well-taught, well-structured technology lesson about building model parachutes will still leave some children retaining the belief that technology refers only to computers and modern high–tech machines.

- Children tend to retain their existing ideas until they are modified or replaced by what they perceive to be better ideas. These existing ideas are not only different from scientific ideas, but can interfere with their subsequent understanding. Learning, therefore, is mainly about changing children's ideas.

- Children can construct an understanding during science lessons by considering new ideas, linking these new ideas to what they already know, and imaginatively restructuring the new with the old. This will only come about if, as noted, the child perceives the new ideas as improvements over previously held ideas.

- Learning new ideas takes time and repetition and any new idea needs to be revisited within a number of contexts to be understood. This reflects the fact that children's existing ideas are strongly held and hard to change, as well as reminds us that new ideas can be difficult to grasp.

- Children need to be physically and mentally involved if they are to advance their understanding of science and technology; hence, they must share responsibility for their own learning with the teacher. Learning cannot proceed without the child's cooperation and effort. Teaching alone does not cause learning; both teachers and children need to play an active role.

The view that learning is more a process of changing ideas than of simply acquiring ideas raises questions as to how and when students' ideas can be changed to move them toward a more scientific or technological understanding. One way you can think of the role of the teacher is as a balancing act. On the one hand, merely telling students new ideas is unlikely to improve their understanding; in fact, it can lead to rote memorization without any understanding. On the other hand, a totally unguided discovery approach is also untenable; it can cause students to become misled and frustrated by trying to figure it all out for themselves, without access to current knowledge that may assist them.

When you consider how to bring students closer to scientific and technological thinking, you should also keep in mind that that there are important differences between children and scientists and technologists. For example, children can be encouraged to act like little scientists and technologists in classrooms but their knowledge and abilities are much more limited than those of adults. Scientific and technological thinking are not just something that children do or acquire automatically but rather require judicious and extended teacher intervention to bring about an enculturation into the scientific and technological worlds.

(Go to your Companion Manual, Textbook Activities 2.1 and 2.2 and think about the possible sources of children's alternative conceptions.)

Rosalind Driver (1941-1997)

The most influential science researcher-educator in the development of constructivist learning theory was Rosalind Driver. Driver started from the strong belief that the most important influence on student science learning was their existing conceptual knowledge. She agreed with Piaget and the cognitivists that students drew on their existing knowledge to explain natural events and that this existing knowledge was often different from current scientific knowledge and hard to change through teaching.

Driver's first novel contribution was suggesting that existing student knowledge, although different from currently accepted scientific ideas, was still internally logical and made sense to the student. Further, that students could use what she called their 'alternative frameworks' to successfully explain what they observed. This diverged from the dominant view that such ideas were random mistakes or misconceptions that just needed correction.

In the 1980s and early 1990s, Driver interviewed children to uncover their existing ideas about various natural phenomena (e.g., light, sound) as well as to find out the consistency of ideas about particular phenomena across a large number of students. She also investigated how students reasoned about natural phenomena based on their alternative frameworks and found student differences linked to variations in age.

Driver explained the development of children's personal understanding using a cognitive constructivist view of learning and her name became closely associated with constructivism. She devised guidelines for changing students' existing ideas through teaching, always giving the teacher a central role in introducing students to scientific ideas while also noting that students would not necessarily interpret what they were taught in ways expected by their teachers. Driver believed it was not helpful to refer to 'constructivist teaching' and preferred to talk in terms of teaching informed by a constructivist view of learning.

From 1989 onwards, Driver advocated a more Vygotskian social constructivist view that emphasized both personal and social factors in science learning. Her work highlighted the importance of language in constructing understanding and the need to establish a 'culture' of science in the classroom. She continued to work on developing effective teaching strategies and studied how student learning progressed in response to various kinds of teacher interventions.

Driver embarked on three more projects later in the 1990s. The first investigated ways that student learning could go beyond conceptual knowledge and also address ideas about the nature of science. The second emphasized the importance of argument in science and of students coming to understand how knowledge claims come to be validated as reliable. The third and last looked at how schools could better foster scientific literacy. Unfortunately, Driver's untimely early death interrupted this new and valuable work.

(Go to your Companion Manual, Textbook Activity 2.3 and think about how children reason from their alternative conceptions.)

Cognitivist and Constructivist Models of Learning

Researchers and educators have developed conceptual models to represent the process of learning, most of which show learning as a series of steps that overlap and interrelate. All conceptual models have their limitations–they can be too simple or too complex, too open-ended or too restrictive. However, used judiciously they can be useful guides to planning and teaching. As you study any learning model you need to think critically about it: What does it explain and what does it leave out? What are its potential advantages and disadvantages to me as a teacher?

Models of learning have come and gone over the years, reflecting changes in educators' perspectives on learning.

Models that have stood the test of time have become part of the science and technology education repertoire, as well as incorporated into later models, so it is useful for you to become familiar with them. Since the 1960s, almost all of them are based on two key models, the cognitivist *Learning Cycle Model (LCM)* and the constructivist *Generative Learning Model (GLM)*.

The Learning Cycle Model

The *Learning Cycle Model* was originally proposed by Robert Karplus (1964) for the SCIS program and is based on Piagetian developmental theory. The model was somewhat atypical of its era because it involved a greater degree of purposeful teacher intervention than the enthusiasts of discovery learning considered appropriate at the time. The overall aim of the model is to help children learn a new concept such as "The wind scatters many seeds" or "Structures can be strengthened by bracing". Later cognitivist models based on the *Learning Cycle Model* changed some terminology and/or incorporated additional phases but the core of the model remains the same.

The Learning Cycle Model has three phases:

- *Exploration:* Students engage in hands-on activities and gather data that raise questions that do not fit their current level of understanding.
- *Concept Invention:* A new concept is introduced under the guidance of the teacher or through another medium to help students summarize their learning, answer their questions, and explain their experiences.
- *Concept Application:* The students apply the new concept to additional examples in order to consolidate their understanding.

Here is an example of the Learning Cycle Model in action:

- *Exploration:* Students test a set of objects to see which float and which sink in water.
- *Concept Invention:* The teacher introduces the concept of buoyancy to summarize and explain the students' experience.
- *Concept Application:* Students are given a ball of modeling clay that sinks. They are challenged to reshape it so that it floats and to explain why.

The Role of Children's Ideas

The rise of constructivism led to some changes in learning models to accommodate the role played by children's existing ideas while retaining the insights embodied in previous models, particularly the *Learning Cycle Model*. The fundamental notion underlying constructivist models is that learning is a complex process of significant *conceptual change* rather than the simple accumulation of new ideas. The teacher's task is to help children change their ideas rather than just to acquire them.

Constructivist models are informed by the identified conditions that facilitate conceptual change. The process begins when children become dissatisfied with their existing ideas. Dissatisfaction can come from the teacher exposing them to situations that prompt them to question their current ideas, for example, through activities with unexpected results (discrepant events). Once children are dissatisfied with their current ideas they may be willing to consider new ideas. Posner, Hewson, Strike, and Gertzog (1982) suggest that new ideas are most likely to be taken seriously if they are intelligible, plausible, and fruitful:

- *Intelligible* means the new ideas make sense to the child and are supported by evidence and reasons.

- *Plausible* means the new ideas can fit with other ideas the child already has.

- *Fruitful* means the new ideas are more useful in explaining the world than the child's existing ideas.

The Generative Learning Model

The *Generative Learning Model (GLM)*, developed by Osborne and Wittrock (1983), was the first comprehensive constructivist learning model in science education. Other models have followed the path blazed by the *GLM* without essentially changing the core conception. The *GLM* has four phases:

- *Preliminary.* Children's existing ideas about a phenomenon or concept are elicited (e.g., through interviews or written surveys).

- *Focus.* Children participate in motivating hands-on activities that help them to explore their existing ideas and present their views to others (e.g., their peers and the teacher).

- *Challenge.* Children discuss, compare, and contrast their ideas on the basis of evidence and argument and are introduced to the scientific idea. They are led to test the validity of their existing ideas as well as the

scientific idea through activities designed to bring them closer to a scientific understanding.

- *Application.* Children use their new more scientific ideas to solve problems in other relevant contexts.

You can see that the three phases of the *Learning Cycle Model* can still be detected within the *GLM*. The key difference is that the *GLM* begins by finding out children's ideas whereas the *Learning Cycle Model* omitted this phase and started by moving children immediately into the exploration of new ideas.

Students' Responsibility for Learning

A very important implication of current learning models is that students must share responsibility for their own learning with the teacher. Students must be willing to take responsibility for attending to lessons and doing the work involved in linking each lesson to existing schema, otherwise little learning will occur. In taking responsibility for their own learning, students should be encouraged to:

- Be engaged by being open about what they think and why they think it.

- Communicate their ideas and thinking to others, both teachers and peers.

- Listen to and value the ideas of others, both teachers and peers.

- Be willing to test the usefulness of their ideas through experimenting, making predictions, and testing technological applications.

- Be willing to consider the merits of the ideas of scientists and technologists even when their own ideas are different.

- Be prepared to change their ideas if the evidence warrants it (e.g., based on experimental outcomes, successful predictions, and technological applications that work).

Implications for Teaching

The constructivist (conceptual change) learning models such as the *GLM* have some very consistent implications for planning and teaching:

- Explore your own ideas about a topic and develop your own understanding before beginning to plan and teach. You need to understand the key concepts and key terms related to the lessons. You need to comprehend the topic well enough to teach and explain concepts to students and feel comfortable handling student questions.

- Structure your unit and lessons carefully and ensure that your unit has a conceptual framework of important ideas that will help students build understanding (see Companion Manual Part D for sample conceptual frameworks). Without a conceptual framework, they are likely to view what is done in classrooms as sets of disconnected activities, each one done for its own sake.

- Think about what is involved in changing students' alternative conceptions about a topic. A good starting point is to think about what it would take to get someone to change *your* ideas. Also, recall that for students to change their ideas they must first be dissatisfied with them and then must be introduced to new ideas that are intelligible, plausible, and fruitful (to them).

- Identify the ideas that the students bring to lessons. This can be done through reviewing relevant research, interviewing students about their ideas, having them complete written surveys, and reflecting on your own teaching experience. Students' ideas can be starting points for building a more scientific and technological understanding.

- Use teaching strategies that encourage students to think about and share their existing ideas. You can begin lessons by finding out what they think rather than moving right into your teaching. This will encourage student to think about their ideas, give you insight into their thinking, and provide you with a starting point when you try to assess how their understanding has changed.

- Provide real and relevant learning contexts. There are many examples of science and technology in students' everyday lives. For example, a lesson on heat could refer to the sun, stoves, furnaces, insulation, thermometers, cooking, vigorous exercise, or having a fever. A familiar context can both motivate learning and be a powerful aid to learning.

- Provide opportunities for group work, discussion, deliberation, and idea sharing, and encourage a classroom atmosphere of mutual respect. It is important to bring ideas out in the open so that others can consider them. This approach also fits with the collaborative aspect of real science and technology.

- Build upon, develop, and restructure students' ideas through experiences with phenomena that incorporate exploratory talk and teacher intervention. Teaching is a delicate balance between what students do and what you do. By reflecting on your own teaching you can become more aware of when and how to intervene and

when to step back and let students work out ideas on their own.

- Enable students to construct knowledge for themselves, including through the use of appropriate scientific and technological knowledge. Students are more likely to learn new ideas when they have been readied through thoughtfully structured learning experiences that take into account their own ideas.

- Use models, metaphors, and analogies to help relate new, unfamiliar knowledge to what is familiar. For example, science learning includes two main kinds of representations, activities and explanations. Explanations are often both unfamiliar and involve invisible phenomena (molecules, electrons, genes, forces) so you need to devise representations that make them visible and familiar.

- Encourage students to make appropriate links between lessons in a unit, lesson ideas and underlying concepts, lessons and everyday experiences, different units and subject areas, and existing ideas and new ideas. Understanding involves seeing the whole, making connections among ideas, and linking learning to life.

- Help students develop an understanding of the nature of knowledge itself, the claims it makes, and how these are validated and may change over time. You need to convey that while our current scientific and technological knowledge is tested and evidentially based, it is also subject to change based on new findings and ideas. Students should realize, for example, that scientific theories are not carved in stone but they are also not 'just theories.'

Language and Drawing

The Importance of Language in Learning

As Vygotsky noted, most important interaction in classrooms, including science and technology classrooms, takes place through language. Both teachers and students spend much of their time talking, writing, and reading. In classroom contexts, language has two main functions: communicating ideas and constructing ideas. Earlier views of language in education focused only on its communicative function whereby teacher and students convey ideas to each other. Newer, more interpretive views place more stress on the connection between language and the active construction of understanding. From this perspective, talking, writing, and reading are seen more as processes of meaning making and less as ways to simply articulate, record, or acquire ideas.

Constructivism and, more specifically, social constructivism place great importance on language experiences in the classroom. As you have seen, social constructivism is largely based on the ideas of Vygotsky, who devoted much of his research to illuminating the connection between thinking and speech. He proposed that thought begins in the child as nonverbal and speech as non-rational. As the child develops, thoughts begin to be expressed through speech and speech structures become the basis of thought structures. Thought and speech eventually merge–thought becomes the internal representation of speech and speech becomes the external representation of thought.

Vygotsky saw language as essentially social rather than individual because it is the means by which human beings both think and communicate with each other. He felt that thought development is determined both by language and by the socio-cultural experience of the child. Language and social experience are interwoven–language is learned through social interaction while social interaction requires the use of language. Vygotsky (1962) summed up this interrelationship as follows: "The child's intellectual growth is contingent on his mastering the social means of thought, that is, language" (p. 51).

(Go to your Companion Manual, Textbook Activity 2.4 and consider how you might help children clarify their understanding of the terms 'heat' and 'temperature'.)

Talking

Classroom science and technology talk includes both teachers and learners. Talk may take different forms–explaining, questioning, discussing, cueing, focusing, and so on. Classroom talk is often dominated by teachers and–desirably or undesirably–often follows a three-step sequence of teacher initiates, students responds, and teacher addresses (e.g., evaluates) student response. Under the influence of social constructivism, teachers are putting more emphasis on children's talk as an important way for students not just to respond to questions but to explore and construct ideas. This mirrors science and technology which are essentially collaborative enterprises involving the exchange and discussion of ideas.

Emphasizing children's talk has several advantages for both teachers and students.

• Emphasis is placed on children's thinking.

• Students are encouraged and enabled to work with ideas in collaboration with others.

• Students are challenged to reach their potential as thinkers.

• When students talk, their thinking becomes accessible to others, both teachers and other students.

More emphasis on student talk also helps alter the balance of classroom power more toward students. In traditional classrooms, teacher talk sets the agenda and student talk only responds to that agenda. When student talk is more about exploring and constructing ideas, students are more in charge of what happens in the classroom and this helps empower them. Talk helps open up the world of science and technology to students by placing their voices more in the foreground of the curriculum.

Similar to how scientists and technologists collectively construct ideas, students can co-construct meaning through organized group talks. The general format is:

• Find out the problem that the students want to investigate.

• Help students to propose ideas that address the problem.

• Students try to find evidence to support or contradict the proposed ideas.

• Students ask and address clarifying questions.

• Students alter or expand the ideas.

Such talks help to expose student's existing ideas and can give insight into how students think and arrive at their conclusions. At the same time, the increased focus on student questions and ideas raises the complex issue of how teachers can balance or reconcile a mandated curriculum with students' interests, since the curriculum may focus on questions other than those that the students want to investigate. (See Chapter 5 for further discussion about balancing students' interests with a mandated curriculum.)

Writing

Language in science and technology takes the form of writing as well as talking. Students need to share their written ideas with others just as they do their spoken ideas. Keep in mind that the main aim of writing, like other classroom activities, is to improve children's understanding. This cannot be accomplished if they simply fill in the blanks or copy what is written on a chalkboard, rather, students must construct meaning by participating in their own learning. Writing must be a tool for thinking, a way for students to actively guide, develop, and express what is on their minds.

Teachers need to provide students with authentic writing tasks that both engage their interest and encourage the manipulation of ideas and images. Here are examples:

- Reporting on scientific work (e.g., summarizing what was learned during a scientific investigation of what is required in a simple electrical circuit).

- Explaining phenomena (e.g., accounting for why a cylindrical column can support more mass than a column shaped like a rectangular prism).

- Writing up experiments or fair tests (e.g., keeping track of what secondary colors result from mixing primary colors while investigating the mixing of colored pigments).

- Outlining the reasoning behind how we know what we know about a phenomenon (e.g., how we know that light will not travel through opaque objects).

- Explaining how a technological device works (e.g., an electric buzzer).

- Describing how a technological device was tested and what were the results (e.g., the results of a test of the strength of a model bridge).

- Discussing what worked and did not work during the development of a technological device (e.g., successes and problems met with while building a vehicle that moves).

Particularly important is writing that focuses on the 'how we know' aspect of learning. This type of writing constructs arguments in support of the reliability of scientific and technological claims by clarifying the means by which they have been produced and validated. It helps students become more aware of the need to base claims on evidence and to think critically, two very important aspects of science and technology.

One difficulty facing teachers and children is that scientific writing is different from other kinds of writing. For example, scientific writing has its own special vocabulary, including unfamiliar words such as "transparent" and "friction". Common words such as "work" are also used in a different way than in everyday life. Scientific and technological writing also has its own structures. For example, certain formats are considered appropriate for writing up experiments (fair tests). If students are to learn scientific and technological

writing, then, the teacher must play an active role. You can help by:

- Giving students writing frameworks or helping them to develop such frameworks.

- Coaching students in required writing skills.

- Allowing students adequate time to draft, improve, and rewrite.

Journals are a recommended and useful tool for classroom writing (and drawing). Journals provide opportunities for children to construct and represent their understanding as well as for teachers to access and assess children's understanding. During a typical lesson, students' journal writing will take different forms:

- Before beginning their investigations and activities, students express their existing ideas, as well as questions they have. They clarify their purposes and requirements, make predictions based on their existing ideas, and plan what they are going to do.

- During their investigations and activities, students mainly focus on, "What is happening?" They collect, record, and organize data, consider alternatives, and interpret their findings and results. They reflect on their existing ideas and questions, as well as record relevant ideas from other sources.

- After their investigations and activities, students mainly focus on explaining and elaborating on their results. They use their evidence as well as current scientific ideas. They may make charts, graphs, diagrams, or concept maps, and introduce ideas from other sources. They discuss their initial predictions and plans, analyze what worked, summarize how their ideas have changed, and apply their learning to other situations.

- Finally, students review and evaluate their investigations and activities and suggest how they might have been conducted differently or improved, as well as suggest further investigations and activities.

Journals also provide opportunities for children to communicate with and share their ideas with others. The journals themselves can be shared or they can be used to create further reports, articles, booklets, or other kinds of presentation. This mirrors the way in which scientists and technologists create reports of their work for presentation to others at conferences or in journal articles.

Reading

Reading should play an important part in science and technology learning for three main reasons.

- Reading is an important activity engaged in by scientists and technologists, keeping them abreast of developments in their field.

- After leaving school, your students are much more likely to engage in science, technology and STS issues by reading than by doing.

- Reading is an activity that many children enjoy and is an important aspect of students' overall education.

Ironically, the current emphasis on an active approach to learning science and technology is often accompanied by decreased emphasis on reading. Reading may be seen as unimportant, outdated, or boring, or even as an impediment to learning in that it prevents students from constructing meaningful understanding through their own explorations. A better way to view reading is that it is an integral aspect of all learning and can play an important role in enhancing and clarifying what students learn through other kinds of activities.

Another reason for neglect of reading is that in the past, text materials have not been very engaging. Newer print materials, however, are much more attractive, interesting, and accessible. Current textbooks tend to have more illustrations, less dense text, fewer words, shorter sentences, and a more attractive design than their predecessors. Science and technology books written for general readers, including children, have also improved in quality and accessibility, and they too can be used in the classroom. Remember, too, that students can read materials other than books, such as newspapers and magazines.

You can use reading in your classroom in a number of ways, for example:

- To access a summary of scientific and technological ideas in order to improve content knowledge.

- To illustrate how scientists and technologists arrive at their ideas, for example, as depicted in biographies and historical accounts of discoveries and inventions.

- To guide practical work in science and technology by initiating it, providing potential explanations for what happened, and elaborating on what happened.

- To self-study science and technology (e.g., by accessing reference materials).

You need to use readings that both engage students' interest and make them think. You should set specific (not general) purposes for their reading, and provide opportunities for them to stop and reflect at critical points. Students should read carefully and consciously interact with what is written (e.g., actively interpret, analyze, synthesize, and criticize what is written, both individually and in small groups). For example,

- When students read about a current scientific theory (e.g., continental drift) you can tell them that it is important to look for evidence that supports the theory (e.g., matching fossils on different continents).

- When students read about a current or new technology you can ask them to think about what are the benefits and risks of that technology.

- When students read about an STS-related issue, you can ask them to find out what scientists agree or disagree on, for example, whether pollution from a factory poses a risk to peoples' health and to the environment.

You can also engage students in directed writing and drawing activities that encourage active reading. For example, students can reconstruct text by figuring out what has been deleted, by placing segments of text in the 'right' order, and by writing predictions of what comes next. They can underline and label text, construct diagrams and tables to represent what is written, answer and set relevant questions, and summarize key points.

(Go to your Companion Manual, Textbook Activity 2.5 and consider the respective roles of scientific and everyday explanations in children's lives.)

Drawing

Drawing, like talking, writing, and reading, is integral to doing science and technology. Drawings and diagrams often accompany written text and help to clarify its meaning. Drawing involves the *visual representation of thinking* (i.e., drawing represents ideas) and, like language, can both represent knowledge and construct meaning. By going beyond words, drawing adds another dimension to the processes whereby students can participate in and articulate their own learning.

Students require little external motivation to draw and the simple instruction to draw something plus the provision of materials is usually enough. The teacher's role is to set the task and provide encouragement. Students can draw real things, things too small to be seen by the naked eye, abstractions, before-and-after pictures, and a series of drawings that show a process or a changing situation. You can integrate talking and writing by interviewing children about the content of their drawings, as well as by having them write explanations of their visual work.

Drawing and Design

Drawing is often referred to as the actual *language* of technological design, the main means by which designers communicate among themselves and with others. In design, drawing plays two very important roles:

- Drawing as a means of *representing ideas* is used to plan projects, sketch emerging forms of a product, and present design ideas to others.

- Drawing as a means of *generating ideas* is used to develop and extend the potential of ideas. This type of drawing is more open-ended and allows for exploration of alternatives.

You need to give children opportunities to use drawings to generate ideas as well as to represent them. Three kinds of drawings are common in technological design:
- Initial sketches that present the core idea behind a design (such as a general shape).
- Working drawings that elaborate on and refine the initial idea.
- Final presentation drawings of a completed project.

The first two kinds of drawings provide rich classroom opportunities for idea generation and development through visual thinking. The final kind of drawing is an effective way to summarize the solving of a technological problem.

(Go to your Companion Manual, Textbook Activity 2.6 and think about how you might use visual representation to help children move toward more scientific conceptions.)

A Final Cautionary Note: Hands On and Minds On

One of the most common misconceptions about teaching science and technology is that if you have students work with hands-on with materials they will automatically understand the related scientific and technological ideas, in other words, that doing equals understanding. This was the key assumption underlying the discovery approach popularized in the 1960s. Both classroom experience and ongoing research have invalidated this assumption.

Even using a constructivist approach, students can do the most carefully structured activities and still emerge with ideas that differ sharply from the understanding that is the learning goal of the activity. For example, students studying light who are asked to explain how they see objects tend to give two different kinds of answers. One response, which is close to the scientific conception, characterizes the eye as a receiver of light. The other response suggests that the eye sees by sending something toward the object, like a ray or other emanation.

It is very apparent that both hands-on activities and **minds-on engagement** are required to help students better understand scientific and technological ideas. Children do need to engage in concrete tasks but at the same time they need the teacher to help them think about and grasp the significance of what happens while they carry out the tasks. Learning in science and technology requires doing but it also requires thinking and that thinking must be aided by thoughtful, appropriate intervention by the teacher.

Thinking Critically About Learning Theories

As we have seen, some of the different theories of how children learn seem to contradict each other. For example, behaviorists view learners as passive, empty vessels waiting to be filled with ideas while constructivists view them as active sense-makers replete with existing ideas. This may make you wonder what you should believe and what you should do in your own classroom.

There is no one best way to teach science and technology, although some ways prove in practice to be better than others do. You can look at learning theory as a work in progress. Researchers and educators are continually proposing and testing new ideas as they try to improve learning and teaching. You can see that in the fact that today's learning theories incorporate a number of ideas proposed by educators in previous eras.

As a teacher, it is good for you to think critically about theories of learning. You should examine the arguments and evidence offered in support of each theory and develop your own views. Rather than accepting a theory of learning because it is new or popular, you should test it out by using it as a guide to planning and teaching and then seeing how well it works in practice in your classroom. Over time, you will develop and refine your views about children's learning and adjust your teaching accordingly. During your teaching career, your own personal theory of learning will continue to undergo changes and improvements based on your new knowledge and experience.

(Go to your Companion Manual, Textbook Activity 2.7 and think about what can be found out about children's learning from studying teacher-student conversations.)

Summary Ideas

This chapter presents some current thinking about:

- *What is meant by understanding.* Understanding, the primary goal of learning, has to do with relating ideas to each other and seeing how they fit together into an integrated whole.

- *What is meant by learning.* In its broadest sense, learning means change. Depending on their perspective, educators have emphasized the importance of changes in student behavior or changes in student thinking.

- *Theories of learning.* Teachers have personal theories of learning that influence how they teach science. Teachers should be aware of the two main kinds of public theories of learning that have influenced education: behaviorist and cognitivist.

- *The behaviorist and cognitive perspectives on learning.* Behaviorists view learning as a process of conditioning–reinforcing desirable student behaviors until they can be demonstrated when required. Cognitivists focus on what goes on in the brain or mind. In cognitivist theories, cognition or thinking replaces observable behavior as the key concept. Learning is seen as the development of thinking and ideas.

- *Contributors to current views of science learning.* Setting the stage for the rise of constructivism, the ideas of five main individuals helped shape our current views of learning in science and technology: Jean Piaget, Robert Gagne, Jerome Bruner, David Ausubel, Lev Vygotsky. Subsequently, Rosalind Driver played a key role in the development of a constructivist view of learning in science education.

- *What constructivism is.* We all construct our own understanding of the world we live in, based on our own experiences. Our understanding is organized into structures of related ideas called schemata that are then used to make sense of subsequent experiences.

Learning is the process by which we modify old schemata or create new schemata, in order to make sense of new experiences.

- *What social constructivism is.* Based on the assumption that children's ideas are influenced by the social and cultural context within which their learning takes place, social constructivism focuses on the social nature of learning. In classrooms, the social context involves interaction with others such as teachers and peers, and the use of language (e.g., discussion, argument, and negotiation).

- *Implications of constructivism.* Learners need to construct their own understanding through a combination of physical and mental activity. Since learners' ideas will not necessarily cohere with scientists' and technologists' ideas, learners need to be helped to find ways to test their ideas through interaction with teachers and peers.

- *Models of learning.* Two main types of models of learning have influenced science education since the 1960s: cognitive models such as the Learning Cycle Model and constructivist models such as the Generative Learning Model. The key difference is that constructivist models explicitly address children's existing ideas prior to teaching.

- *Importance of language and drawing experiences to learning.* Language in classrooms functions both to communicate ideas and to construct ideas. Talking, writing, and reading are currently seen more as processes of meaning making and less as ways to simply articulate, record, or acquire ideas. Drawing is an important aspect of both scientific inquiry and technological problem-solving and serves as a visual representation of thinking. Drawing is used to both generate and represent ideas and may reveal understandings not shown by text.

- *Thinking about theories of learning.* Theories of learning need to be addressed critically and tested in practice.

Making Productive Connections
Scenario

You have just been hired as an elementary teacher. Your principal asks you to prepare a science lesson on buoyancy that takes a constructivist approach. What would your lesson plan look like? How does your plan address the implications for constructivist science teaching outlined in this chapter?

Article

In, 'The construction of scientific knowledge in school classrooms' (Millar [Ed.], 1989, p. 104-105), Rosalind Driver states: *"There will always be the questions of judgment for teachers about how far a pupil may be helped to progress in his or her understanding, about when and how to intervene."* How would you as a teacher develop the kind of judgment that Driver refers to? What would you need to know and be able to do? During a particular science lesson, what clues might you look for to suggest that you should intervene?

Ideas to Think About When Teaching Science, Technology, and Society

- *What do I understand about the topic I am teaching?*
- *What are the currently accepted ideas about the topic I am teaching?*
- *What are the existing ideas that my students have about the topic I am teaching?*
- How do my students' ideas about the topic differ from the currently accepted?
- What teaching strategies could be useful in helping my students gain a better understanding of the topic I am teaching?

Selected Readings

Brooks, J., & Brooks, M. (2001). *In Search of Understanding: The Case for Constructivist Classrooms.* Upper Saddle River, NJ: Prentice Hall.

This book builds a case for a constructivist approach to teaching and learning in all classrooms.

Driver, R., Guesne, E., & Tiberghien, A. (Eds.). (1985). *Children's Ideas in Science.* Milton Keynes: Open University Press.

This book discusses constructivism in science education in the context of specific science topics, with particular reference to children's ideas.

Driver, R., Asoko, H., Leach, J., Mortimer, E., & Scott, P. (1994). Constructing scientific knowledge in the classroom. *Educational Researcher* 23, 5-12.

This article presents a constructivist perspective on learning in science and discusses the implications of this perspective for teaching and learning in classrooms.

Osborne, R., & Freyberg, P. (Eds.) (1985). *Learning in Science: The Implications of Children's Science.* New Zealand: Heinemann.

This early book analyzes the significance of the finding that children bring their own views of science and the meanings of words to science learning, and the effect this has on what and how they learn.

Selected Websites

DR. JOHN LAWRENCE BENCZE, ONTARIO INSTITUTE FOR STUDIES IN EDUCATION (OISE), TORONTO: CONSTRUCTIVISM
http://www.oise.utoronto.ca/~lbencze/Constructivism.html
This site provides a summary of constructivism and a number of links to related sites.

INDIANA UNIVERSITY/ERIC CLEARINGHOUSE
http://www.indiana.edu/~ericrec/ieo/bibs/cons-ele.html
This website contains a comprehensive bibliography of materials from the World Wide Web, ERIC Database, and other sources intended to provide an introduction to constructivism.

NOVA SOUTHEASTERN UNIVERSITY: LEARNING THEORY RESOURCES: A COLLECTION
http://www.nova.edu/~burmeist/learning_theory.html
This website provides a wide variety of links to learning theory sites.

PENN STATE UNIVERSITY COLLEGE OF EDUCATION
http://www.ed.psu.edu/ci/Journals/97pap1.htm
This article outlines how to effectively incorporate reading into hands-on science activities. An extensive bibliography of other useful articles is included.

SAN JOSE STATE: ELECTRONIC JOURNAL OF LITERACY THROUGH SCIENCE (EJLTS)
http://sweeneyhall.sjsu.edu/ejlts/
This online journal publishes articles on language development and science education, bilingualism and science education, and scientific literacy.

TIP (GEORGE WASHINGTON UNIVERSITY): THE THEORIES
www.gwu.edu/~tip/theories.html
This website provides information on a wide variety of learning theories.

UNIVERSITY OF COLORADO AT BOULDER: WRITING IN SCIENCE

http://stripe.colorado.edu/~carpenh/sciwritebib.html

This site includes links to sites on science writing and a comprehensive bibliography.

VIRGINIA ASSOCIATION OF SCIENCE TEACHERS: CONSTRUCTIVISM

http://www.pen.k12.va.us/Pav/Va_Assoc_Sci/construct3.html

This site provides links to a number of sites and article relevant to constructivism.

DR. MARGARET WATERMAN, BIOLOGY DEPARTMENT, SOUTHEAST MISSOULA STATE UNIVERSITY

http://cstl.semo.edu/waterman/SE320AltCert/altcert/alternativeconc.html

This website provides links to sites about children's alternative conceptions in science.

Chapter 3
Building Blocks of STS: Concepts, Skills, and Attitudes

Learning Objectives

- In this chapter, you should learn about
- The importance of scientific inquiry.
- The importance of technological problem-solving.
- The importance of STS decision-making.
- How concepts, skills, and attitudes are commonly described.

Thinking About Your Existing Ideas

Write down your answers to the following questions. After you complete this chapter, revisit your answers. Which of your ideas remained the same and which changed? How did they change, and what do you believe caused the changes?

- What do you think children should learn in science class?
- How would you define the terms "concepts," "skills," and "attitudes"?
- How would you describe "scientific inquiry"?
- What would scientific inquiry look like in an elementary classroom?
- What does it mean to "strike a balance between science as inquiry and science as a common body of knowledge"?
- What do you think children should learn during technological problem-solving?
- How would you describe "technological problem-solving"?
- What would technological problem-solving look like in an elementary classroom?
- How would you describe "STS decision-making"?
- What would STS decision-making look like in an elementary classroom?

As you saw in Chapter 1, ideas about science and technology are influenced by social, cultural, and political contexts. Some ideas fade over time (e.g., teaching that science is objective), while others show impressive staying power (e.g., teaching about scientific inquiry). You will be teaching during a time when standardized science programs are gaining in popularity, so it is likely that what you teach will be strongly influenced by provincial or national standards. In North America, programs of study tend to reflect many similar ideas about what students should know. For example, the *Common Framework of Science Learning Outcomes* (Council of Ministers of Education, Canada, 1997) contains standards similar to the American *National Science Education Standards* (NRC, 1996). Authors of these documents divide these standards into concepts students should know and accompanying skills and attitudes they should develop through participation in scientific inquiry and technological problem-solving, and STS decision-making.

A key idea when considering concepts, skills, and attitudes is that lessons should contain all three of these important elements or building blocks. Science is a body of common knowledge expressed as concepts. Skills are used to construct and validate scientific knowledge. Attitudes reflect the changing, creative, and social nature of science. Technology also has a knowledge base expressed as concepts, involves skills associated with designing and making, and is created through the development of attitudes such as curiosity and persistence. The intertwining of these elements is important both as a teaching strategy and in presenting an authentic image of the scientific enterprise and technological problem-solving. (To think about how teachers' beliefs about science can influence teaching, go to the Companion Manual and do Textbook Activity 3.1.)

What is Scientific Inquiry?

Recognition of the importance of teaching children science through inquiry first appeared in science education writings in the early part of the 20th century. The idea continued to be endorsed through the 1960s, and it now infuses recommendations in content standards documents and is part of the framework of many science-teaching resources. In classrooms, scientific inquiry is an instructional strategy that involves the process of seeking answers to questions, including questions brought to the classroom by the teacher and questions that arise out of activities. In scientific inquiry,

this search for answers frequently involves posing further questions, identifying assumptions, making observations, researching related information, planning investigations, gathering data, proposing answers, considering alternative explanations, andcommunicating results (CMEC, 1997). Clearly, scientific inquiry is action oriented (hands-on and minds-on); educators believe that by using this instructional strategy teachers can help children develop an understanding of how science happens and the ability to use skills (e.g., observation skills and critical and logical thinking skills) and develop attitudes (e.g., open-mindedness) associated with science. Also, through inquiry children can move towards understanding scientific concepts and the connections between concepts.

Myths About Scientific Inquiry

The National Research Council (2000, pp. 35-37) recognizes that many myths abound about inquiry. These myths affect the kinds of lesson plans teachers write for students and the teaching strategies they select to teach science. These myths include the following:

- *Scientific inquiry can be taught without attention to subject matter.* This myth likely arose from science programs that advocated a view of inquiry that involved a focus on skill development to the virtual exclusion of subject matter. Current ideas about inquiry maintain that skills cannot be separated from content or context.

- *All science subject matter should be taught using a hands-on approach.* Using a hands-on approach (e.g., having children inquire using kit-based instructional materials) to science in every lesson would give students the impression that this is the only way to scientific knowledge. Not only would this misrepresent the nature of science and scientific inquiry, but would ignore the fact that science is both a body of knowledge and careful, systematic inquiry.

- *Inquiry teaching occurs easily through use of hands-on or kit-based instructional materials. Student engagement in hands-on activities guarantees that inquiry teaching and learning are occurring.* The use of hands-on materials does not guarantee inquiry is happening any more than it guarantees that the students are constructing a meaningful understanding of concepts related to the activities. Teachers are always needed to facilitate how materials are used and how students think about those materials.

- *True inquiry occurs only when students generate and pursue their own questions.* Questions can come from any number of resources including the teacher, the students, reading materials, friends, and so on. The source of the question does not determine whether or not inquiry is happening.

(To think about the critical role of conceptual knowledge in scientific reasoning, go to the Companion Manual and do Textbook Activity 3.2.)

A Need for Balance

Children do not always have to do hands-on activities in order to construct an understanding of science concepts. Instead, "teachers should use different strategies [and not just a single teaching approach] to develop the knowledge, understandings, and abilities described in the content standards. Conducting hands-on science activities does not guarantee inquiry, nor is reading about science incompatible with inquiry" (NRC, 1996, p. 23). A balance between hands-on activities and other teaching strategies such as reading better reflects what science is—a body of knowledge and careful, systematic inquiry. (See Chapter 4 for discussion of the range of teaching strategies you can use to teach science to children.)

What is Technological Problem-Solving?

In classrooms, technological problem-solving is an instructional strategy that focuses around having students design and make a model of a technological object (e.g., playground equipment, boat, tower, vehicle, electrical device, glider) according to a set of guidelines (e.g., The tower should be 1 meter high and support a film canister of sand.). As mentioned in Chapter 1, technological problem-solving lessons involve identifying some human want or need, formulating specifications for the technological solution, generating alternative ideas and proposals, selecting and implementing a final solution, and evaluating that solution. Although these tasks may initially appear to be logical sequential steps, research shows that technological problem-solving is characterized by iterative thinking, where design roadblocks and constraints lead to students re-thinking their designs and essentially 'going back to the drawing board' before they ever reach some final solution. Clearly, technological problem-solving is action oriented (e.g., hands-on and minds-on); educators believe that having students participate in technological problem-solving will help them develop an understanding of how technology happens and the ability to understand technological concepts (e.g., ideas about structural strength and stability), use skills (e.g., manipulative skills), and develop attitudes (e.g., inventiveness).

What is STS Decision-Making?

STS decision-making is an instructional strategy that involves the consideration of science and technology-related social issues, with the intention of coming to a defensible decision as to what might reasonably be done about the issue. The various considerations that speak for and against possible alternative courses of action are assessed, weighed, and evaluated en route to reaching the decision to act. STS decision-making introduces into the study of science and technology the societal question, "Should we do this?" with the rationale that:

- Science and technology influence many individual and social issues as well as affect the environment, thus students need to develop an understanding of these interactions.

- History demonstrates that scientific and technological developments may have detrimental effects, thus students need to appreciate both the contributions and limitations of science and technology in helping us try to resolve societal and environmental issues wisely.

There are a great many potential STS issues, some of which have lingered for decades (e.g., global warming). Others, like genetically modified organisms and foods (GMOs) have become controversial topics only in recent years. STS issues may be general to society or specific to a certain geographical area. With so many possibilities, the main considerations for educators have more to do with pedagogy than availability. In selecting STS issues, teachers should ask:

- Can the issue be linked to the Program of Studies?
- Will my students be interested in and concerned about the issue?
- Can the issue be readily researched and studied by my students?
- Will my students be capable of grasping the science and technology that is related to the issue?

Some Common Ideas About Concepts

Concepts are the content or knowledge that children learn as they progress through different grade levels or divisions (e.g., K–3). Science programs typically include opportunities for children to examine concepts drawn from life science (e.g., ecology and biology), physical science (e.g., properties of matter, light, sound, heat, magnetism, and forces and movement), and earth and space science (e.g., geology and astronomy). Technology components of science programs tend to ask children to explore concepts related to the properties of materials, tools, strength, stability, structures, and movement. The term "concept" can sometimes be a source of confusion because different authors define it in different ways. In this textbook:

> **A concept is a statement of important knowledge underpinning children's scientific inquiry, or technological problem solving, or STS decision-making.**

Consider the concept "Living things require water for the use and maintenance of their parts." Note that this concept is a statement of scientific knowledge about living things and water and is an important idea that could underpin any number of scientific inquiry activities involving plants and animals. If the same concept appears in a number of activities, then you can use it to link those activities in an educationally significant manner. (See Chapter 5 for discussion of how to plan using concepts to link activities. See Companion Manual Part D for concepts related to the Alberta program.)

General and Specific Concepts

Concepts are on a continuum from the more general to the more specific. For example, the concept "Living things are distinct from nonliving things because of the essential processes which sustain them" is more general than the supporting, more specific concepts "Living things use oxygen in the process of generating energy," "Living things require water for the use and maintenance

of their parts," and "Living things have mechanisms for the removal of waste."

Concepts Versus Contexts

Concepts are not the same as *contexts*. For example, the concept "Living things have mechanisms for the removal of waste" could be explored within a number of contexts, such as looking at stomata on leaves, examining human skin, or exploring the functions of lungs and kidneys. These different contexts could be tied together using the important idea stated by the concept.

Unifying Concepts

All concepts are to some extent unifying in that they can be used to link different events and activities; however, science program authors usually begin by describing what they believe to be fundamental unifying concepts–concepts that can be used to link different scientific disciplines (e.g., link life science to physical science). Unifying concepts are expressed as a series of words (e.g., "Systems, Order, and Organization") and act as conceptual tools that will allow you and your students to bring together diverse areas of the natural and human-made world. In order to generate a list of unifying concepts, authors had to ask themselves a key question— What words can be used to describe and connect the big, overall picture of scientific knowledge? Tables 3.1 and 3.2 show that program authors in the United States and Canada generated similar lists of unifying concepts

Table 3.1
American National Science Education
Standards: Unifying Concepts

Unifying Concepts	Rationale
Systems, Order, and Organization	Natural and designed worlds are large, complex, and interrelated. To study this complicated reality, scientists define smaller units of investigation referred to as systems. Analyzing systems allows scientists to interpret the world.
Evidence, Models, and Explanations	Evidence enables scientists to develop explanatory models and construct more sophisticated explanations for phenomena.
Constancy, Change, and Measurement	Through measuring system elements, scientists have found that some things are in the process of change (e.g., earth's surface) while others are characterized by constancy (e.g., speed of light).
Evolution and Equilibrium	Evolution accounts for the present form and function of objects. Equilibrium is a physical state in which forces and changes occur in opposite and off-setting directions.
Form and Function	Form of an object or system is related to function and function frequently relies on form.
	Adapted from NRC, 1996, p. 116-119.

Table 3.2 Canadian Common Framework
of Science Learning Outcomes:
Unifying Concepts

Unifying Concepts	Rationale
Systems and Interactions	Thinking about the world in terms of its parts and alternately about parts in terms of how they relate to one another and to the whole allows scientists to understand and interpret the world.
Constancy and Change	Some characteristics of materials and systems remain constant over time (e.g., the speed of light) whereas other characteristics change (e.g., earth's surface).
Energy	Energy, whether transmitted or transformed, is the driving force of both movement and change.
Similarity and Diversity	Attributes of materials or events help to make useful distinctions between one type of material or event and another.
	Adapted from Council of Ministers of Education, 1997, p. 16

Both tables 3.1 and 3.2 show that program authors began with the premise that the world is large, complex, and interrelated. They asked themselves, "How can scientists study this overwhelming complexity?" and then answered, "Through studying smaller, less complex pieces and using the knowledge gained to speculate about the whole." Therefore, both lists mention how scientists order the world, think about parts of the world, and sometimes create models to enhance their understanding of the world. Important to understanding the world and creating order and organization is the ability to recognize similarity and diversity among objects, organisms, and systems. Scientists must be able to make distinctions between one type of event and another and understand the different functions of and relationships among objects, organisms, and systems. Both tables also include the ideas that the world is characterized by change (e.g., evolutionary change, behavioral change, energy that changes from one form to another, matter that changes from one state to another, objects that change position, and changes to the earth's surface) and constancy (e.g., the charge of an electron and the speed of light are constants). (To get a sense of how concepts can be arranged to show connections, go to the Companion Manual and do Textbook Activity 3.3.)

Some Common Ideas About Skills

Skills are the cognitive, procedural, and manipulative tools children use during scientific inquiry, technological problem-solving, and STS decision-making–for example, communicating, analyzing and synthesizing data, and defending conclusions. In science programs, skills have been given many labels–*process skills, basic process skills, integrated process skills, thinking skills, and basic processes*, to name just a few. As you can see, the word "process" is frequently attached to "skills"–a combination reminiscent of the phrase "science as process," as discussed by Robert Gagne (1965) in the SAPA curriculum project (see the discussion of Gagne in Chapter 2). Other authors have argued that raising questions and making observations involve processing ideas and information, and therefore these skills can reasonably be described as process skills (Harlen, 2000). In many programs of study, skills are called process skills and are inextricably linked to conceptual understanding, Millar and Driver (1987) remind us that the skills themselves are not the aim of classroom instruction but the vehicles by which students can develop a more effective understanding of scientific and technological concepts, the purposes of science and technology, and their links to society. In this textbook, we will simply use the term "skills" to describe children's cognitive and procedural thinking, and manipulative work.

Current Ideas About Skills in Scientific Inquiry

In the past few decades, educators have held a variety of ideas about skills and their place in science programs. In the following sections, we summarize the most recent thinking about skills.

- *Skills associated with scientific inquiry are not unique to science.* Although skills play an important part in scientific inquiry and in the development of scientific understanding, they are characteristics of logical thought in general (Millar & Driver, 1987). Skills such as predicting, analyzing, communicating, and observing are used in many fields to solve problems and answer questions. For example, artists, architects, and store clerks observe, classify, and communicate as part of their jobs. Scientific thinking, therefore, is not characterized by these skills but by the way students using these skills employ scientific concepts to answer scientific questions.

- *Skills cannot be separated from content or context.* In science education, content is used to teach skills and skills are used to teach content—each is necessary. The intertwining of content and skills is important both as a pedagogical strategy and in presenting an authentic image of the nature of science. In the past, some educators argued that skills could be separated from context (Gagne, 1965). For example, they believed that if you trained children to classify leaves, they could then use this skill in any other scientific context that required classification skills. Science programs that reflected this belief highlighted lists of basic and integrated process skills and put an emphasis on training children to develop these general skills. Content was given less emphasis. Current research has shown that the transferability of a skill to some new context is crucially dependent on the learner's perception of whether the new context is close to the context in which it was formerly applied (Millar & Driver, 1987). Although skills may appear to be general, teachers need to be mindful that students' perceptions of content and context affect performance–that is, whether they can apply the skills productively.

- *Skills are guided by students' existing ideas.* Students enter classrooms with existing ideas that influence how they inquire into scientific questions. For example, think about students looking through a microscope at small moving objects in a drop of pond water. It is likely that the students will be able to describe and agree upon the shapes of the moving objects, the relative speed of the objects, and the general characteristics of the objects. Other aspects of the moving objects such as whether they can be classified as plants or animals or whether the objects share some common characteristics might be less clear and more open to debate. Millar and Driver (1987) explain: "what observers initially 'see things as' depends not only on the features in the stimulus situation but also on their prior learning and the classification available to them through language" (p. 48). In the pond water example, the acts of observing and classifying were limited by the nature of sensory impressions and influenced by what each student already knew about observing, classifying, and small moving objects.

- *Skills presented in lists may suggest a linear sequence beginning with a question and ending with a conclusion.* Scientific inquiry, however, tends to be characterized by recursive or iterative thinking. In the past, students were encouraged to follow the scientific method—make observations and collect facts, analyze and classify these facts, and derive generalizations and conclusions. Science programs that reflected a belief in this view of science would list these skills in some logical order, and teachers would interpret this list as a linear series of stages constituting the scientific method. In the NSE Standards, authors advise that although the skills "suggest a logical progression, they do not imply a rigid approach to scientific inquiry" (p. 144).

Scientific inquiry features different mixes and sequences of skills, depending on the context of the investigation, the students' prior understandings, and events during the investigation. For example, analyzing data may lead to conclusions or it may cause students to rethink the investigation and to plan on doing it in another way. Similarly, planning an investigation could result in students reconsidering the question and perhaps reconfiguring it. Scientific inquiry, therefore, can involve going back and forth between skills (iterative thinking) and revisiting earlier stages of the investigation (recursive thinking) rather than a linear progression.

- *Students should develop manipulative, cognitive, and procedural skills.* Manipulative skills are the fine and gross motor skills needed to work with materials, objects, and instruments during the course of scientific investigations. Cognitive skills include those that allow students to formulate hypotheses, think critically about the investigation, draw analogies, analyze and synthesize data, and offer conclusions. Procedural skills are used when students are planning what to do, carrying out the plan of action, deliberating about what to do next, and deciding when to conclude an investigation. All of these skills are interrelated and dependent on each other. Communication and teamwork, and the students' existing knowledge, are essential components of how these skills are used by students.

- *Cognitive skills are a set of generalizable operations for developing reliable knowledge.* Cognitive skills can be classified into four main groups – observing, communicating, interpreting data and experimenting (conducting fair tests) (see Table 3.3).

**Table 3.3 Common Cognitive Skills
in Scientific Inquiry**

Observation Skills

Observing	Gathering information about objects or events using the five senses.
Measuring	Making quantitative observations of properties of objects or events.
Classifying	Grouping objects or events according to common properties.

Communication Skills

Communicating	Recording observations or data in forms that can be understood (e.g., charts, tables, graphs, and diagrams). Communicating information to other people in order to generate, share, and refine ideas.

Interpretation Skills

Interpreting	Identifying relationships and patterns in collections of objects or events.
Inferring	Making an observation and then inferring the possible meaning of the observation. Usually an inference is narrow in scope and frequently paired with an observation. For example, picking up a heavy object, feeling the weight of the object, and inferring the object is made of iron.
Generalizing	Making broad statements that apply to most, if not all, cases.
Formulating Hypotheses (Tentative Explanations)	Proposing tentative, testable explanations for a set of events based on previous observations and inferences. Using the "If … then…" format where the 'If" part is what is done and the "Then" part is what will happen.
Predicting	Using existing data, proposing inferences and patterns to suggest future outcomes.
Formulating Models	Creating physical or conceptual models to describe the behavior of an unfamiliar object or event in terms of something that is familiar.
Defining Operationally	Defining objects and events through describing the action performed on the event or object and what was observed.

Experimentation (Fair Test) Skills

Experimenting	Designing and carrying out a controlled investigation (fair test).
Controlling Variables	Identifying factors that influence the outcome of an experiment and manipulating one variable in a structured manner to demonstrate its effect.

Scientific Inquiry Skills in Grades K–3

The following list of skill statements is commonly described in K-3 programs of study:

- *Asking questions about objects, organisms, and events in the environment.* Students should be encouraged to ask questions about phenomena related to their lives and environment. They should be helped to ask questions that arise from predictions (forecasts of future events based on existing understanding) or involve an explanation that can be tested (e.g., a hypothesis in which students formulate a possible explanation for some event–frequently students use the format "If [I do this]…then [this will happen]" to state their hypotheses).

- *Researching related information.* Students should be helped to extend their background knowledge of the question. They should access print materials, the Internet, and hypermedia resources to find out what scientists already know about the question. Information gained should be used to aid investigation, data interpretation, and data analysis and should help to extend the results to some limited range of application.

- *Planning simple investigations.* Students should be encouraged to make a prediction or formulate a hypothesis about the outcome of the investigation. They should be helped to plan how they might find answers to their questions and make decisions about what to look for to obtain results. Most plans will

Figure 3.1
Designing Experiments (Fair Tests)

Experiments, or fair tests, involve identifying and manipulating variables in a logical manner to demonstrate their effect. An experiment designed to compare the rate of germination of two brands of radish seeds would take the following form:

Problem or Question:
Which radish seed has a higher rate of germination—Brand #1 or Brand #2?

Hypothesis:
Based on what is known about the germination rate of these two brands of seeds, what might be a testable explanation for this experiment? For example, "If 10 seeds of each brand are planted and all the seeds are cared for properly, then the brand that has the largest seeds will sprout at a higher rate and have the higher rate of germination".

Types of Variables:
- *Responding or dependent variable.* The factor that represents the result, or measured change, that occurs because of the influence of other factors (e.g., the number of seeds of each brand that germinate).
- *Manipulated or independent variable.* The factor that is systematically altered to see how it influences the responding variable (e.g., the brand of radish seeds).
- *Controlled variables, or variables held constant.* The variables that are kept the same while another is manipulated (e.g., use the same number of seeds, same type of soil, same planting depth, same watering conditions, and keep constant such environmental factors as light, temperature, humidity, and wind).
- *Uncontrolled variables.* Factors that are knowingly or unknowingly ignored in the hope that their effects are insignificant (e.g., an environmental factor such as one set of plants being placed in a slightly draftier classroom location).

Experimental Design, or Procedure:
What should be done before, during, and after the experiment in order to test the question?

Recording the Data:
What should be done before and during the experiment in order to gather data pertinent to the question?

Communicating Conclusions:
What tentative conclusion or explanation can be given with regard to the initial problem or question?

involve some investigation that depends upon systematic observations (gathering information using as many of the five senses as appropriate). In later grades, students can plan experiments (or fair tests) in which some variables are controlled while one is manipulated (see Figure 3.1).

- *Employing simple equipment and tools to gather data and extend the senses.* Students should be helped to gather evidence related to their questions by making observations and manipulating materials and tools. They should measure distance, weight, time, and height using standard units (e.g., grams or centimeters) and nonstandard units (e.g., blocks or the length of a hand). Students should use tools (e.g., hand lenses, rulers, stopwatches, spring scales, beam balances, microscopes, and thermometers) to enhance their observations. They should use computers and calculators, where appropriate, to conduct investigations and record data.

- *Recording the data.* Students should be encouraged to record data in some systematic way. They can draw pictures of objects and events, maintain records of sequences such as life cycles, compile lists, and attempt some simple classification systems (e.g., selecting or grouping objects or events according to some common property). They can construct graphs (e.g., showing plant growth over time), tables, and bar charts to show comparisons among objects or events. They can write anecdotal records of observations to augment information represented in other ways. Students should be assisted to think about how best to present data so that the data can be interpreted and communicated to others.

- *Using data to construct a reasonable explanation.* Students should be helped to analyze and interpret data, by identifying patterns or regularities. They should begin to understand what constitutes evidence and be able to justify their interpretations by referring to the evidence. Students should be asked to write about the thoughts and reasons behind their interpretations and draw connections between cause and effect (especially in the case of experiments, or fair tests). At times, it may be appropriate to ask students to formulate operational definitions (e.g., defining some object or event through describing the action performed on the event or object and what was observed). For example, a textbook definition of oxygen would be, "Oxygen is a nonmetallic element; the chemical symbol is O," while an operational definition would be, "Oxygen is a gas that can cause a smoldering wooden splint to burst into flame."

- *Evaluating and concluding.* Students should draw conclusions, propose explanations, and write about how their ideas are supported by evidence. They should identify and write about unifying ideas that link their investigation to others. Students should compare their ideas to scientific explanations and check their results and explanations against those obtained by other students.

- *Communicating and sharing ideas.* Students should communicate how they conducted the investigation, the evidence they gathered, and the conclusions they came to. They should be able to defend their ideas by referring to evidence gathered in written or pictorial form and should be able to recognize error or uncertainty in their results. Students should discuss alternative approaches to the investigation and consider how their results could lead to further investigations.

Scientific Inquiry Skills in Grades 4-7

The following list of skill statements is commonly described in 4-7 programs of study:

- *Asking questions that can be answered through scientific investigations.* Students should be encouraged to ask questions and recognize the difference between questions that can be investigated through hands-on activities and those that cannot. They should be helped to refine and refocus ill-defined questions to turn them into questions that can be investigated. This involves analyzing questions for the variables involved and identifying productive questions related to those variables. For example, a question such as "Why do mirrors reflect light?" can be turned into a number of questions that can be investigated, such as "What kinds of surfaces reflect light?" "At what angles can light be reflected?" and "How does the shape of a mirror influence light reflection?" Students should be helped to understand that different kinds of questions call for different kinds of investigations (e.g., questions that can be answered by observing, manipulating materials, surveying, or collecting print data). Students should begin to consider what makes a question scientific.

- *Researching related information.* Students should be expected to extend their background knowledge related to the question. They should access print materials, the Internet, and hypermedia resources to find out what scientists already know about the question. Information gained should be used to aid investigation, data interpretation, and data analysis, and should help them extend the results to a broad range of applications.

- *Designing scientific investigations.* Students should be helped to clarify their existing ideas about the question and compare these ideas to current scientific knowledge. They should be expected to make predictions about the outcome of an investigation or formulate hypotheses that can be tested. Students should be helped to maintain a balance between questions that can lead to investigations and those that can be explored using experiments (fair tests). They should be able to analyze questions and quickly identify variables (manipulated, responding, controlled, and uncontrolled variables) involved in an experiment (fair test). Students should be able to make decisions about what data would constitute a result and justify those decisions to others. They should be able to design an investigation or experiment relevant to the question.

- *Conducting scientific investigations.* Students should be expected to follow their plan for an investigation or experiment. They should use systematic observation, refine observations using instruments where necessary, and make measurements using appropriate instruments. Students should record additional questions that arise during an investigation or experiment.

- *Using appropriate tools and techniques to gather, analyze, and interpret data.* Students should be expected to gather evidence related to their questions by making observations and manipulating materials and tools. They should measure distance, weight, time, and height using standard units (e.g., grams or centimeters). Students should use tools (e.g., hand lenses, rulers, stopwatches, spring scales, beam balances, microscopes, and thermometers) to enhance their observations. They should use computers and calculators, when appropriate, to conduct investigations and to record, summarize, and display data.

- *Using mathematics in all aspects of scientific inquiry.* Students should be able to use mathematics to refine observations (e.g., to provide more precise measurements) and to gather (e.g., counting a variety of populations), organize (e.g., calculating population density), and present (e.g., in bar graphs and tables) data. They should use mathematics to seek patterns or regularities in the data and to justify conclusions.

- *Recording the data. Students should be expected to record data in a systematic way.* They can draw pictures of objects and events, maintain records of sequences (e.g., plant growth over several months), compile lists, and construct classification systems (e.g., construct dichotomous categories for grouping various kinds of plants and animals). They should construct graphs, tables, and charts to show comparisons between objects or events. They should write anecdotal records of observations to augment information represented in other ways. Students should know how best to present data so that the data can be interpreted and communicated to others. They should use computer hardware and software designed for recording and displaying data (e.g., spreadsheets and computer graphics).

- *Developing descriptions, explanations, and models using evidence.* Students should seek patterns or regularities in the results and use this information to construct explanations and conclusions based on evidence. They should check their results and consider the value of repeating tests to add reliability to their data. Students should recognize sources of error or uncertainty in their results and assess whether these factors reduce the validity of their claims. Students should revisit the scientific information they accessed prior to conducting the investigation or experiment and use this information to support and explain their results. They should write about the thoughts and reasons behind their interpretations and draw connections between cause and effect.

- *Thinking critically and logically to make relationships between evidence and investigations.* Students should reexamine their assumptions about cause and effect. They should reexamine any anomalous data (data that do not agree with their interpretations) and consider reasons behind the emergence of these data. Students should think critically about their question, procedures, methods of data collection, and explanations. They should consider whether different approaches to answering the question might have produced other, more reliable results.

- *Evaluating and concluding.* Students should draw conclusions, propose explanations, and write about how their ideas are supported by evidence. They should identify and write about unifying ideas that link their investigation to others. Students should compare their ideas to scientific explanations and check their results and explanations against those obtained by other students.

• *Recognizing and analyzing alternative explanations and predictions.* Students should listen to ideas proposed by others and consider how those ideas compare to their own. They should question other students' explanations in a respectful manner and evaluate those explanations by examining data, reconstructing reasoning, and suggesting alternative explanations. Students should reexamine their own conclusions in light of ideas presented by other students.

• *Communicating scientific procedures and explanations.* Students should communicate how they conducted the investigation, the evidence they gathered, and the conclusions they came to. They should be able to defend their ideas by referring to evidence gathered in written or pictorial form and should be a ble to recognize error or uncertainty in their results. Students should discuss alternative approaches to the investigation and consider how their results could lead to further investigations.

(To get a sense for how skills can appear in a common science lesson, go to the Companion Manual and do Textbook Activity 3.4.)

Current Ideas About Skills in Technological Problem-Solving

Much technology education research has focused on characterizing what children do while solving technological problems and arranging these actions or skills into problem-solving models. Various terms have been used to describe children's problem-solving actions—*skills, processes, facets of performance, thinking processes, procedural skills, and abilities of technological design,* to name just a few. Regardless of the label given to children's actions, when researchers arrange these actions into problem-solving models they tend to include skills such as designing, planning, making, troubleshooting, evaluating, and communicating. The following list summarizes the most recent thinking about these skills:

• *Skills cannot be separated out from content or context.* In technology education, researchers have proposed that the skills children select to solve a technological problem and the ways in which they use those skills are influenced by the context of the problem (McCormick et al., 1993; Kimbell et al., 1996). This context can, in part, include the subject matter of the task, the degree of structure present in the task setting, and the opportunity for iteration between action and reflection (Kimbell et al., 1996). For example, if students are encouraged to identify authentic problems that are personally meaningful to them (i.e., if they can relate the problem to a need and can see the value of their activity), then they are more likely to suggest a variety of solutions, tackle ongoing dilemmas, and solve difficulties creatively (Hennessy and Murphy, 1999). The classroom context and students' expectations can also strongly influence the way in which they carry out technological problem solving (Jones, 1997). For instance, if students are working in a classroom in which they are encouraged to collaborate with others, then they are likely to continue collaborating during technological problem solving tasks. Teachers, the majority of whom do not possess a technological background, clearly play a critical role in setting problem and classroom contexts that influence students' skill usage (Jones 1997).

• *Skill usage is informed by a range of interconnected knowledge.* McCormick (1997) has identified a range of interconnected knowledge that influences how students use skills to solve technological problems. Procedural knowledge is "knowing how to do it" knowledge and is characterized by the skills students use to solve problems (e.g., designing, modeling, planning, and evaluating). Many researchers use the terms procedural knowledge and procedural skills interchangeably. Conceptual knowledge ("knowing that" knowledge) makes possible the effective use of procedural knowledge. For example, knowing that gears can be joined together and that certain combinations of gears can result in a change of direction or speed can inform how students design model vehicles. Strategic knowledge (knowing how to decide what to do and when) can be developed only through explicit teaching. For example, students must be taught to break down global tasks into smaller subtasks and think through the sequence of joining tasks together.

• *Skills are guided by children's existing ideas.* Students enter classrooms with existing ideas about technology and how it works, and these ideas influence how they go about solving technological problems. These existing ideas may prove helpful or unhelpful when children encounter and then try to resolve a technological problem.

• *Skills presented in technological problem solving models tend to be characterized by recursive or iterative thinking.* Technological problem-solving can be characterized as iteration between action (e.g., drawing, modeling, making) and reflection (e.g., identifying issues for judgment and identifying strengths and weakness of proposed designs). Other times, researchers present a view of technological problem-solving that is characterized by recursive thinking. Proponents of both views agree that the way students use skills when solving technological problems is not straightforward. For example, trying to join wheels to an axle may result in difficulties that require students to revisit their original design decisions. Evaluating the load capacity of a paper straw bridge may result in students returning to think again about design constraints. Technological problem-solving, therefore, is not characterized by a linear progression, but rather it involves going back and forth between action and reflection (iterative thinking) or even revisiting earlier stages of the design process (recursive thinking).

- *Students should develop manipulative, cognitive, and procedural skills.* Manipulative skills involve the fine and gross motor skills needed to work with materials and construct devices and products (e.g., cutting, joining, and drilling). Cognitive skills are inextricably linked with procedural skills; together they allow students to identify a problem, propose design solutions, construct a device or product, troubleshoot difficulties, critically evaluate the design, and communicate procedures and results to others.

Technological Problem-Solving Skills in Grades K–3

The following list of skill statements is commonly found in K-3 programs of study:

- *Identifying a simple problem.* Students should be able to draw on their own experiences to identify a problem and the need that gave rise to the problem. They should be encouraged to identify how they might solve the problem and talk about how the problem is linked to what we value as a society.

- *Proposing a solution.* Students should be able to plan what to do to solve the problem. They should prepare a variety of design proposals (e.g., drawings and descriptions of those drawings) and identify the constraints influencing each proposal (e.g., constraints such as cost, materials, time, space, and safety). Students should be helped to break the task down to smaller subtasks and understand the task sequence needed to construct the device or product.

- *Implementing proposed solutions.* Students should be helped to develop the ability to work collaboratively with other students to accomplish the task. They

should be assisted to use materials (e.g., wood, cardboard, plastic, and metal) and tools (e.g., scissors, hole punches, screwdrivers, drills, hammers, and saws) to construct their device or product. They should be helped to understand which tools to use with certain materials (e.g., use scissors with paper, light cardboard, and thin, flexible plastics). Students should be helped to understand that troubleshooting (analyzing difficulties and proposing solutions to overcome these difficulties) is an inevitable part of designing and making. They should be helped to share their problems and work with others to resolve the difficulties. Students should understand that ongoing planning can change the original plans. They should be encouraged to keep records of design changes (e.g., using pictures, labeled drawings, and short explanatory writing).

- *Evaluating a product or design.* Students should use a variety of criteria to evaluate the acceptability and suitability of the devices or products. Criteria include asking if the product is durable (does it stand up to repeated use?), cost effective (is it easy to make? does it use inexpensive materials?), effective (does it work?), reliable (does it work every time?), and safe (are there any risks involved in using the product or device?). Also, does the product or device have an effect on the environment (does it use natural materials or recyclable or biodegradable materials? what will happen when it is no longer useful or wanted?), and what are the risks and benefits of the product or device? Students should be helped to consider how the product or device could be improved and think about other applications for it.

- *Communicating a problem, design, and solution.* Students should communicate how they designed, made, and evaluated the product or device using oral, pictorial, and written communication. Written reports of design changes made and the reasons behind the design changes should be encouraged.

Technological Problem-Solving Skills in Grades 4–7

The following list of skill statements is commonly found in 4-7 programs of study:

- *Identifying appropriate problems for technological design.* Students should identify a problem and the need that gave rise to the problem. They should consider various aspects of the problem and the need for collecting information relevant to the problem and making appropriate use of a range of references (e.g., talking to relevant people such as the user or client and other experts and accessing print information and the Internet). Students should investigate real situations related to the problem and discuss what values are reflected in the need for the product or device. They should share their existing ideas about the proposed product or device, especially as regards materials and methods that might be used during construction.

- *Designing a solution or product.* Students should be encouraged to plan how to construct the device or product. They should prepare a variety of design proposals and present these proposals using verbal, written, and pictorial communication. For each proposal, students should consider constraints (e.g., cost, time, trade-offs, materials, and human safety) and identify design criteria (e.g., the load the structure must carry, the terrain over which a vehicle must move, or the elements the clothing must protect you from). They should consider how science concepts could inform the design (e.g., ideas about friction can influence how wheels are joined to axles). Students should work out in advance any manufacturing issues (e.g., what materials to use, how to join parts together, the sequence in which to join parts together, and what tools to use with different materials). They should plan with others how to break down the task into smaller subtasks. They should draw and label a picture of the intended design and write about how the design will fulfill the need. Students should talk to others about their final design decisions and record the thinking behind their decisions.

- *Implementing a proposed solution.* Students should have the ability to work collaboratively with other students to accomplish the task. They should be reminded how to use materials (e.g., wood, cardboard, plastic, and metal) and tools (e.g., scissors, hole punches, screwdrivers, drills, hammers, and saws) to construct their device or product. They should know which tools to use with certain materials (e.g., use scissors with paper, light cardboard, and thin, flexible plastics; use a saw on wood). Students should know that troubleshooting is an inevitable part of designing and making. They should share their problems and work with others to resolve difficulties. Students should understand that ongoing planning can change the original plans and they should be expected to keep records of design changes (e.g., using pictures, labeled drawings, and explanatory writing) and the reasons underlying these modifications. Students should keep records of their ongoing evaluation of the evolving design.

- *Evaluating completed technological designs or products.* Students should use a variety of criteria to evaluate the acceptability and suitability of the device or product. Criteria include asking if the product is durable (does it stand up to repeated use?), cost effective (is it easy to make? does it use inexpensive materials?), effective (does it work?), reliable (does it work every time?), and safe (are there any risks involved in using the product or device?). Also, does the product have an effect on the environment (does it use natural materials or recyclable or biodegradable materials? what will happen when it is no longer useful or wanted?), and what are the risks and benefits of the device? Students should consider how the product or device could be improved and think about other applications for it.

- *Communicating the process of technological design.* Students should communicate how they designed, made, and evaluated the product or device using oral, pictorial, and written communication. Written reports of design changes made and the reasons behind the design changes should be expected.

Current Ideas About Skills in STS Decision–Making

Some STS decision-making research has focused on describing the skills needed to synthesize and interpret information, identify different points of view, and arrive at a personal stance that may or may not require some course of action. Researchers primarily describe cognitive skills (e.g., organizing information and communicating that information to others) as being key to participating in STS decision-making. Similar to scientific inquiry and technological problem-solving skills,

- Skills cannot be separated out from content or context.

- Skills are guided by children's existing conceptions.

- Skills tend to be characterized by recursive or iterative thinking.

STS Decision-Making Skills in Grades K-7

The following list of skill statements is commonly found in K-7 programs of study:

- *Understanding the issue by locating and organizing information.* Students should develop the ability to locate science, technology, and society information related to the issue under study. They should use the Internet, computer programs, print resources, surveys, and the library in their search for information.

Students should be helped to assess the reliability and validity of their information sources and understand that not all sources of information carry equal weight.

- *Identifying alternatives.* Students should identify relevant interest groups (stakeholders). They should consider the scientific and technological knowledge that might help lead to a decision about what action to take.

- *Analyzing and synthesizing information.* Students should compare and contrast different points of view. They should identify the perspectives of relevant stakeholder groups. After listing several potential courses of action, they should identify the potential consequences of different courses of action.

- *Deciding on a course of action.* Students should attempt to build a consensus in favor of a particular course of action.

- *Taking action* Students should show responsibility for their decision by taking personal action. They should show responsibility for their own actions as members of a group.

- *Evaluating actions and decision-making.* Students should evaluate the effects of their actions and evaluate the decision-making process.

Some Common Ideas About Attitudes

Attitudes describe the characteristics children should try to develop through in-school and out-of-school experiences–for example, curiosity, sensitivity to the environment, willingness to listen to classmates, willingness to question their own preconceived ideas, and resolve to base their ideas on evidence. Attitudes affect how children engage in their school science and technology experiences and, ultimately, how well they understand scientific, technological, and STS concepts. For example, children who are willing to look at scientific data from more than one perspective, listen to others, and thoughtfully reflect on their own perceptions are more likely to construct a meaningful understanding of scientific concepts.

Scientific Inquiry Attitudes in Grades K-7

Closely related to the ability to use a range of skills is the willingness to use them (Harlen, 2000; Harlen & Jelly, 1989). This means a willingness to ask questions about the natural world, engage in scientific inquiry, and think about interpretations and conclusions. The school, along

with parents and other institutions, seeks to help students develop attitudes and values that ultimately affect scientific understanding. Attitudes that are commonly associated with scientific inquiry include:

- *Showing curiosity about the natural world* (e.g., asking questions about objects and events, being interested in a broad range of scientific fields and issues, and showing interest in the outcomes of scientific activity).

- *Using critical thinking* (e.g., examining anomalous data, drawing connections between evidence and conclusions, and thinking about how an investigation could have been done differently).

- *Showing perseverance* (e.g., maintaining interest in an investigation for a considerable length of time, repeating a test that appeared to fail the first time, and completing an investigation even though others have long finished the activity).

- *Displaying open-mindedness* (e.g., listening to and respecting other students' ideas, being willing to modify conclusions in light of new evidence, and not being dogmatic).

- *Showing respect for evidence* (e.g., using evidence to justify conclusions and changing ideas in response to evidence).

- *Being willing to work with others* (e.g., sharing activities and experiences with classmates, appreciating the benefits gained from a shared effort, and being willing to work with a diverse group of classmates).

- *Developing moral sensitivity* (e.g., developing a sensitivity to the environment and a commitment to care for the environment and living things, including other people).

- *Being honest and accurate* (e.g., reporting the results that emerged from the investigation [not what you hoped would happen], showing how accurate measurements were made, and seeking reliable sources of background information).

- *Appreciating that diverse people from a variety of countries and cultural backgrounds have contributed to science* (e.g., appreciating that science has been conducted throughout history by men and women from a variety of countries).

Technological Problem-Solving Attitudes in Grades K-7

Attitudes are distinct from skills and concepts in that they describe a willingness to act in a certain way (Harlen & Jelly, 1989). Connections between concepts, skills, and attitudes become apparent, however, when teachers observe that skill development and conceptual understanding are critically influenced by students' willingness to consider and undertake technological tasks. Attitudes that are commonly associated with technological problem solving include:

- *Displaying inventiveness* (e.g., generating new ideas using materials in unusual or constructive ways, and suggesting new designs, methods, or applications).

- *Showing curiosity for the manufactured world* (e.g., asking questions about devices and products, wondering how things work, and showing interest in the outcomes of technological problem solving).

- *Showing confidence in technological abilities* (e.g., independently collecting materials, working with tools, and proposing a variety of designs).

- *Showing perseverance* (e.g., trying a variety of ways to join parts together, being willing to troubleshoot to solve difficulties, and completing construction even if others have long finished the activity).

- *Being willing to work with others* (e.g., sharing designing and building with classmates, appreciating the benefits gained from a shared effort, and being willing to work with a diverse group of classmates).

- *Developing moral sensitivity* (e.g., sensitivity to how technology reflects what society values and sensitivity to impacts on the environment and on other living things).

- *Taking personal responsibility* (e.g., taking responsibility for one's actions, being unwilling to lay blame on others for design failure, and stating one's own responsibility within the group).

- *Developing empathy for the challenge of invention* (e.g., empathy for the procedures, frustrations, and lives of inventors).

(To get a sense for how attitudes may appear in a common technological teaching context, go to the Companion Manual and do Textbook Activity 3.5.)

STS Decision-Making Attitudes in Grades K-7

Attitudes in STS decision-making are related to those needed for responsible citizenship. Attitudes describe a willingness to think and act in ways that lead to knowledgeable, balanced decision-making that takes into consideration the rights of others.

- *Showing respect and tolerance* (e.g., respecting the opinions of individuals and groups in local, national, and global communities).

- *Being responsible towards the environment and the community* (e.g., understanding that personal choices and actions impact on the larger community).

- *Being willing to work with others* (e.g., choosing to work with diverse groups who may not share similar views).

- *Respecting the rights and opinions of others* (e.g., listening to diverse groups and considering other opinions with respect to your own).

Concepts, skills, and attitudes comprise the building blocks of scientific inquiry, technological problem-solving, and STS decision-making. Teaching strategies should emphasize the development of these building blocks, plans should include all three building blocks, and assessment should be designed to allow teachers to judge to what degree children are developing concepts, skills, and attitudes. (To get a sense of how the Alberta Elementary Science Program (1996) is organized, turn to the Companion Manual and do Textbook Activity 3.6.)

Summary Ideas

This chapter discusses scientific inquiry, technological problem-solving, and STS decision-making and provides information about the concepts, skills, and attitudes that make up the framework of school programs. The chapter presents some current thinking about:

- *The importance of scientific inquiry.* Scientific inquiry refers to the diverse ways in which scientists study the natural world. Children who pose questions, identify existing ideas, research related information, plan investigations, gather and analyze data, propose answers, and consider alternative explanations are practicing inquiry. Educators believe that by using this instructional strategy, teachers can help children develop skills, attitudes, concepts, and an understanding of how science happens.

- *The importance of technological problem-solving.* Technological problem-solving refers to the diverse ways in which technologists build technological devices to address human wants and needs. Children who identify a need, design a number of possible solutions, select a final solution and evaluate that solution are practicing technological problem-solving. Educators believe that by using this instructional strategy, teachers can help children develop skills, attitudes, concepts, and an understanding of how technology happens.

- *The importance of STS decision-making.* STS decision-making involves the consideration of science and technology-related social issues, with the intention of coming to a defensible decision as to what might be reasonably done about the issue. Children who gather information about an issue, analyze that information, identify alternative solutions, and decide on a course of action are practicing STS decision-making. Educators believe that by using this instructional strategy, teachers can help children develop concepts, skills, and attitudes and an understanding of how STS decision-making happens.

- *What students should know.* Students need to understand scientific and technological concepts and grow towards the goals of scientific and technological literacy. They need to be willing to use various skills to develop that understanding and achieve those goals. Concepts, skills, and attitudes make up the framework of many North American programs.

- *How concepts are defined.* A concept is a statement of important knowledge underpinning children's scientific inquiry, technological problem solving, and STS decision-making.

- *How skills are defined.* Skills are the cognitive, procedural, and manipulative tools children use during scientific inquiry, technological problem-solving, and STS decision-making.

- *How attitudes are defined.* Attitudes are the characteristics children should try to develop through in-school and out-of-school experiences—for example, a willingness to listen to classmates.

Making Productive Connections

Scenario 1

You have just been hired as an elementary teacher but you know that you have a very modest understanding of scientific concepts. What will you do to develop your subject matter knowledge so that you can support your students' inquiry into science?

Scenario 2

The children in your Grade 1 class are unwilling to listen to science ideas expressed by other children. How will you help them develop this attitude that is critical to the construction of a meaningful understanding of technological concepts?

Ideas to Think About When Teaching Science, Technology, and Society

- How do I plan my units to help students understand connections between concepts?
- How do I include my students' existing ideas in my daily teaching strategies?
- How do I include skills in each of my lessons?
- How do I help students develop attitudes in each of my lessons?
- How do I help my students understand the differences between scientific inquiry and technological problem-solving?
- How do I include topics of local interest in my science program?

Selected Readings

Harlen, W., and Jelly, S. (1989). *Developing Science in the Primary Classroom.* Essex: Oliver & Boyd.

The authors provide an overview of basic ideas related to planning for teaching, working with children, organizing a classroom, developing children's ideas, and assessing children's learning.

Kimbell, R., Stables, K. & Green, R. (1996). *Understanding Practice in Design and Technology.* Buckingham: Open University.

The authors present an overview of how U.K. educators view technological activities in schools. They discuss technology and human endeavor, technological tasks and activities, progression, and the U.K. National Curriculum. Particularly useful are their descriptions of technological skills.

National Research Council (2000). *Inquiry and the National Science Education Standards.* Washington, D.C.: National Academy Press.

The authors provide information about how science inquiry might look in classrooms, how inquiry is characterized in the *NSE Standards*, and how to assess children in inquiry classrooms. They also provide a rationale for the importance of inquiry teaching and learning.

Selected Websites

KEY SCIENCE CONCEPTS
http://www.sasked.gov.sk.ca/docs/elemsci/menu_ksc.html
This website provides a list of science concepts commonly taught in Saskatchewan schools. Compare this list to those found in your own program of studies.

SCIENCE FRAMEWORK FOR CALIFORNIA PUBLIC SCHOOLS
http://www.cde.ca.gov/ci/science.html
This website provides a copy of the science framework for California public schools. Consider what is expected in these schools and compare these expectations to those found in your own program of studies.

Chapter 4
Instructional Strategies in STS

Learning Objectives

In this chapter you should learn about

- The manner of teaching.
- How to manage students.
- The three key instructional strategies for teaching science, technology, and STS: scientific inquiry, technological problem-solving, and STS decision-making.
- Other general teaching strategies you can use within the three key strategies.

Thinking About Your Existing Ideas

Write down your answers to the following questions. After you complete this chapter, revisit your answers. Which of your ideas remained the same and which changed? How did they change, and what do you believe caused the changes?

- What is teaching?
- How should teachers organize and manage classrooms for teaching?
- How should scientific inquiry be taught?
- How should technological problem-solving be taught?
- How should STS decision-making be taught?

This chapter builds on ideas from previous chapters and presents a range of teaching strategies to help children develop scientific and technological literacy. The recommended strategies focus around three main instructional strategies–scientific inquiry, technological problem-solving, and STS decision-making. Each of these instructional strategies is composed of essential elements that comprise the overall picture of the strategy. In order to teach these elements, teachers select from a variety of teaching strategies, including discussion, questioning, and demonstration. This chapter also integrates ideas from previous chapters about the nature of science and technology, how children learn, and the organization of teaching goals around concepts, skills, and attitudes.

Your first extended teaching opportunity as a preservice teacher will likely occur during your student teaching practicum. As you consider the ideas in this chapter, think about some of the questions that you may have in anticipation of your practicum:

- How will I know what strategies to use for particular lessons?
- How can I interest students in the lesson?
- How can I organize students for group work?
- What kinds of interventions can I use to support and direct students?
- How will I know when to intervene to support a student and when to step back?
- If at the end of the lesson the students share a variety of scientific and unscientific ideas, what should I do?

Understanding Teaching

Effective Teaching

The main goal of teaching is learning and the effectiveness or success of teaching is often judged by how well students learn. Learning may be assessed in various ways but one common measurement, particularly in the current climate of 'accountability', is scores on standardized achievement tests (note: standardized achievement tests are critically examined in Chapter 6). The reasoning seems logical: when scores are high teachers are assumed to have taught effectively and when scores are low, they have not. Research on effective teaching looks for teacher behaviors that correlate with increased student learning. These teacher behaviors are usually generic rather than subject-specific, and are said to apply to teaching in general. For example, in order to be effective, teachers are advised to structure their

lessons, keep classroom interaction moving at a brisk pace, ask a lot of questions, and set aside time for student independent practice.

The effective teaching research is helpful but it also raises questions about at least two important instructional issues:

- How should we teach to bring about the intended learning goals?
- What is the role of subject matter knowledge in teaching?

Both questions warrant serious consideration and keeping them in mind can help guide you through the many ideas about instructional and teaching strategies that are discussed in this chapter.

The Manner of Teaching

Our commonsense notion is that teaching is a practical activity that intends learning, i.e., a change in the learner's thinking. We say "intends" because we know planned learning goals may not always be (completely) achieved even with the teacher's best efforts. There are also other related activities that intend to change thinking that we do not call teaching. One example is propagandizing, which implies a one-way transmission where the receiver plays a passive, accepting role. You can distinguish teaching from such undesirable relatives by acknowledging that teaching has a certain manner associated with how learning is brought about. The essential core is that teaching must be conducted in a way that *respects the thinking and ideas of those being taught.* For example, teachers (and students) need to provide evidence and reasons for their claims, ask and address questions, honour objections, and respect alternative points of view.

The manner of teaching distinguishes it from two undesirable extremes, *indoctrination and abandonment.* Indoctrination means we are concerned only with leading the student to the desired goal–for example, an explanation for why materials expand when heated–without a concern that they arrive at the goal based on evidence and reasons. Our whole focus is the right answer with no regard to how the answer is reached. Indoctrinated students holding their ideas unthinkingly. For example, instead of concluding that the earth is round because ships sailing to the horizon appear to sink, they conclude that the earth is round because the teacher, the textbook, or the scientist says so. Such students are incapable of inquiring critically into the validity of their beliefs and reject any evidence that contradicts them, even though they may still score high marks answering related questions on an achievement test!

Abandonment, the opposite of indoctrination, is also a danger and means eliminating meaningful teacher intervention in student learning. The teacher leaves students to discover everything for themselves, based on the assumption that students can build up all required scientific knowledge by manipulating materials, observing what happens, and then drawing the right conclusions (See Chapter 2 for more information on discovery learning). Our scientific knowledge includes many important classification schemes (e.g., Linnaean classification system for living organisms), theories (e.g., plate tectonics), and models (e.g., models of chemical reactions) that scientists have developed using creativity and insight and which cannot be derived directly from observable events. For example, students may observe many interesting things about animal structure and behaviour but, unaided, it is extremely unlikely they will come up with the theory of natural selection.

Balance is required to avoid both indoctrination and abandonment. Teaching involves knowing when to intervene to help students develop scientific ideas and when to step back and let students investigate and try to construct ideas on their own. You can think of teaching as balancing on a continuum between commonly accepted ideas and student ideas. Determining when, where, and how to intervene to assist student learning is an ability developed through classroom practice and reflection on practice.

The Teaching-Learning Connection

The intent of teaching is learning. It is hard to think of one without the other; teaching without learning becomes pointless while learning without teaching is limited in scope. What is the nature of the teaching-learning connection? One possibility is that the link is direct—teaching causes learning and if learning does not occur then the teacher has not taught (or has taught poorly). Experience, however, demonstrates that classroom life is not so simple and there are many factors that influence both teaching and learning, from individual attentiveness to socioeconomic background. This is clear from the fact that a teacher may teach a class of thirty and some students will learn while others will not.

A more realistic view is that the teaching-learning connection is indirect. Teachers may still teach in the sense of intending learning, even though (some) students–for various reasons–may not learn. Teaching cannot cause learning directly but can bring about mental and physical involvement on the part of the student that leads to learning. Such involvement includes students

- Engaging in active investigation.
- Inquiring into events.
- Developing concepts and skills to make sense of their experiences.
- Reflecting on how and why their ideas have changed.
- Becoming aware of their own learning.
- Assessing the effectiveness of their participation in learning.
- Determining ways to improve how they learn.

Learning, then, is the result of students' mental and physical involvement (hands on, minds on) rather than the direct result of teaching. The teacher teaches in a way that the student can eventually take hold of the learning and "put it all together", avoiding both indoctrination and abandonment. This conception of the teaching-learning connection addresses the fact that while you can have students do a myriad of activities–collect data, make charts, answer questions, draw diagrams–you cannot make them learn. Learning only occurs with the active compliance of the student; the student must decide to learn and try to learn. From this perspective, teaching is very important and necessary, however, learning is not solely the teacher's responsibility but the joint responsibility of teacher and students (see Chapter 2 for more on the Student's Responsibility for Learning.)

(To think about what teaching is, turn to your Companion Manual and complete Textbook Activity 4.1)

Teacher Functions

To try to realize your intent of bringing about student learning, you will fulfill a great variety of functions in the course of your daily classroom teaching: explaining, asking questions, cueing, motivating, supervising, marking assignments, handing out materials, taking attendance, and so on. Some functions are more important to learning than others (e.g., explaining is more important than taking attendance). Key to understanding teaching is to focus on the functions most essential to learning. These can be divided into two broad groups:

- Managing ideas.
- Managing students.

Teacher functions related to managing ideas contribute most directly to learning and focus around major concepts of a topic, how the concepts are organized, students' existing ideas, how investigation into the topic is carried out, and how knowledge claims arising from investigations are tested. Teacher functions relating to managing students contribute less directly to learning and have the overall aim of placing and keeping learners in a state that makes it possible for learning to occur (e.g., arousing interest, focusing attention, and keeping on task).

Both managing ideas and managing students are necessary to learning and experienced teachers orchestrate them simultaneously. Our discussion will first consider how teachers manage students. Later we will consider how teachers manage ideas during scientific inquiry, technological problem-solving, and STS decision-making.

Managing Students

As a beginning teacher, keeping students mentally and physically engaged will be one of your dominant concerns. You will wonder if students will:

- Pay attention and listen.
- Cooperate by carrying out learning activities.
- Thoughtfully participate in bringing about their own learning.

Keep in mind that learning and management are not separate issues; the better you manage ideas, the less you have to manage students. Management approaches rooted in behaviorism emphasize establishing routines, setting up a classroom management system, and dealing with misbehavior. While these issues need consideration, the context of teaching is also very important. A cognitive approach to management emphasizes influencing students to think about and positively affect their own behavior. It is more likely that students engaged in challenging, interesting science investigations at their own level will stay focused and pose fewer management problems.

You should not confuse management with discipline. Discipline is administered after the breakdown of

management leads to inappropriate student behavior like disruption, defiance, and aggression. A strictly behavioral approach would suggest that misbehaviour is best addressed by identifying the problem behavior, recording how often and under what conditions it occurs, and positively reinforcing desired behavior. Weaknesses of this approach are that it:

(a) May change the behavior but gives little insight into its cause.

(b) Involves a high degree of control and manipulation.

Arranging the Classroom

Physical organization of your classroom aids management. Student seating is an important consideration and you can try various configurations.

- Traditional rows.
- Partners seated side by side.
- Groupings of four desks.
- Scattered tables with chairs.
- One large circle of desks.

Your seating plan will depend on factors such as teacher preference, classroom composition (e.g., age, split grade classes), and learning goals (e.g., developing skills and attitudes through group work). Safety (e.g., access to exits) and student disabilities (e.g., wheelchair accessibility) are also important considerations. Many teachers change seating plans during the year, as well as move individual students to different locations. You can also change your own seating (i.e., you can move your desk to different locations in relation to your students) in order to change the dynamics of your classroom (e.g., moving from the front of the classroom to the side where you are less in view).

You may decide to set up one or more science learning centres around your classroom perimeter. Centres comprise sets of instructions and materials to carry out tasks and provide students with opportunities to work independently on program topics. For example, while studying simple machines you might set up a centre where students take apart a toy that integrates one or more simple machines, draw a diagram explaining how the toy works, and then correctly reassemble it. Centres may be used for enrichment or each student in the class can be systematically rotated through the centre while the rest of the class engages in other activities

Routines

Routines, which are expected procedures for carrying out class activities, are another aid to management. When you begin with a new class you need to establish certain routines to help everything run smoothly. Eliciting student input into these routines will give students a sense of ownership and increase their compliance. Students who are familiar with routines are more likely to participate productively and less likely to create problems. Be sure that students understand the importance of each routine and be alert for the need to revisit or change certain routines later in the year. Routines are helpful for

- Starting the day. For example, having students take turns taking attendance.

- Transitions between lessons or parts of lessons. For example, having students move quietly and quickly from a whole class discussion into small group work.

- Distributing materials, collecting materials, and cleaning up. For example, having one student in each group take responsibility for handing out drawing paper.

- Signaling for attention. For example, flicking the lights on and off or doing responsive cadence clapping when you feel the noise level is negatively affecting learning.

- Moving around and leaving the room. For example, having students put a name tag on a hook when leaving the room.

- Finishing early. For example, having students who finish their work early ask others who are not done if they need help, check their classroom agendas for other tasks they need to do, or move to independent work at a science centre.

Grouping or Cooperative Learning

Classroom grouping for teaching generally alternates between whole class and small groups. At times it will be important for you to teach the whole class. For example when:

- Introducing a lesson.
- Eliciting students' existing ideas using a survey.
- Giving instructions.
- Clarifying difficulties common to all students.
- Sharing experiences.
- Demonstrating.
- Presenting alternatives.

Even in whole class situations you should emphasize teacher-student and student-student interaction. For example, when reviewing student observations, elicit them from individual groups and students. Resolve contradictory observations by having students view each other's data, discuss with each other possible reasons for disparities, and perhaps observe each other repeat the data collection.

Education currently emphasizes the importance of social interaction during learning so you will also want to place students in small groups to carry out their work collaboratively. When managed properly, groups can learn more effectively than individuals, however, groups do not just happen. To be successful, they need to be well organized and effectively monitored. When organizing groups it is recommended that you

- Place 3-5 students in each group. There will be enough members to develop meaningful interaction but not so many that some become passive.

- Ensure members understand their responsibilities. For example, members should focus on the task, present their ideas, listen to the ideas of others, and carry out agreed upon decisions.

- Assign members with roles. Typical roles include managing materials, recording data, and cleaning up.

- Change group members as required. Factors to consider include gender, personality, and getting along with others.

- Allow student input into group organization and function. For example, students can help decide what roles would be appropriate for group members.

When monitoring small groups, it is recommended that you

- Ensure groups record their data and ideas (e.g., by checking to see that charts are completed).

- Check that members are fulfilling their responsibilities (e.g., by asking students to report on how well their group is functioning).

- Check progress by soliciting feedback (e.g., by asking students during technological problem-solving what problems they have encountered and how they have overcome their problems.).

- Intervene as necessary to promote thinking, collaboration, and learning (e.g., by asking students why they are doing what they are doing, encouraging students to consider each others' ideas, and getting students to summarize their work).

Resources

Hands-on, minds-on activities require appropriate materials and equipment. You should know what resources are currently available at your school, as well as what dependable sources are near your school, e.g., the local drugstore (refer to Appendices A, B, C, and D for more information). Efficient storage of what you have and accurate record-keeping are a must. If you are in charge of materials, know who your suppliers are and order what is needed well in advance. Replace anything that is used up as soon as possible (e.g., chemicals, paper straws, and aluminum foil).

Before doing an activity with your students, try it yourself. This will avoid unpleasant surprises such as the activity not working as planned once you are in front of your class. If possible, set up materials and equipment before class begins. You can have students take turns helping you with setup and clean up. A wheeled cart moves materials and equipment efficiently from storage to the classroom. Ensure students understand required safety precautions and know how to use everything properly (refer to the information in Appendix A). Prior to each lesson, teach essential skills such as measuring so students do not become frustrated by a physical inability to carry out their investigations.

Keep students away from materials and equipment until you have completed your preliminary instructions, otherwise they will be distracted from what you are saying. One approach is to have materials and equipment set up at a number of stations away from where students are seated when you instruct them. Having one more station than you have student groups will increase time on task. When you need to meet again with the whole class to share results and ideas, bring them to a location away from the materials and equipment–such as a carpeted area at the front of the room–so that they can attend fully to the discussion.

You can substitute commonly available materials and equipment for their harder-to-get scientific counterparts. For example, vinegar is a weak solution of acetic acid and a kitchen measuring cup works as a beaker. Finally, keep in mind that activities do not need to be based on sophisticated equipment and spectacular effects to achieve your teaching goals. In fact, in terms of learning, such intricacy is often more diversionary than helpful.

Classroom Climate

An appropriate classroom climate contributes significantly to classroom management. This can begin with the physical appearance of the room, e.g., bulletin boards, wall posters, and displays of student work. Most important is the affective climate, which may take time to establish. Your science classroom is a social setting where students should feel welcome, comfortable, and secure. You need to be supportive and encouraging and help students feel they are valued as persons and that they are contributing meaningfully to classroom life (e.g., you can have students answer each other's questions). This approach fits with our identified manner of teaching, that teaching should respect the ideas and thinking of students. It also fits with an authentic image of science and technology as requiring active, thinking participation.

Flow

Flow is a useful concept in classroom management and is described as a sense of ongoing classroom rhythm, engagement, and anticipation where learners feel in control of their own circumstances. Classrooms flow when teachers

- Stay aware at all times (e.g., by being aware of which students are on task).
- Start the class immediately with learning activities (e.g., by posing a challenging question that provokes thinking).
- Maintain a high level of student interest (e.g., by using examples relevant to everyday life).
- Keep students alert and involved (e.g., by getting a member of each group engaged in a task to report on how the group is progressing).
- Give concise and brisk instructions (e.g., "Your task is to draw two possible ways that you could use the tacks and the paper clip to make a switch").
- Avoid interruptions once students are working (e.g., by clarifying all necessary instructions before students become involved in their work).
- Make smooth transitions during lessons and between lessons (e.g., "I want you to stop what you are doing at your tables, put down your materials, and come over and sit on the carpet facing me").
- Move around the room and monitor classroom activity (e.g., by observing how much of the task each group has completed).

- Handle individual disruptions without interrupting the rest of the class (e.g., by taking a student aside and discussing a problem in private).
- Redirect misbehavior before it happens (e.g., by noticing that one group will finish well before the others and making sure they are aware of what they should do next).

Time

Time management is a must because time is your most precious resource and there is never enough. One reason is that elementary teachers have so many things to do (e.g., plan lessons, find materials, mark assignments, preview audiovisual materials, prepare report cards, meet with parents). Another reason is that the traditional school emphasis on language arts and mathematics that may lead to the neglect of science and technology. Finally, there is so much to learn in science and technology that teachers can begin to think that they just will not be able to properly address the curriculum. To deal with time pressure you should

- Accept that you can only accomplish so much (e.g., you will never have enough time to address every single student question about a topic; if you can answer just a few questions in each unit, this is a good beginning).
- Run your classroom efficiently to conserve available time resources (e.g., spend a minimum of time on transitions between lessons).
- Understand that more is less (e.g., it is better to teach a few concepts well than many of them poorly).
- Teach students how to learn themselves and encourage them to go beyond their classroom instruction (e.g., get students to do research at home to answer some of their own questions).
- Meaningfully integrate science and technology with other subjects (e.g., use time assigned to mathematics to teach measurement, use time assigned to art to teach scale drawings).

Outside the Classroom

You can also teach science and technology outside of the classroom walls (e.g., in the schoolyard, at a pond, and in science and technology museums). These environments provide unique learning opportunities (e.g., interaction with organisms in their natural setting or access to historical artifacts). They also encourage students to think of learning as being more than what occurs in the classroom. Taking students outside the classroom may also create additional management issues and the key is to plan ahead and prepare for the experience. Teachers should

- Visit the route or destination ahead of time.
- Plan what students will do or, if possible, have students themselves research the planned experience.
- Ensure student activities include observation and data collection.
- Let students know what to expect and what they are supposed to do.
- Inform students of any additional expectations and responsibilities.
- Allot the time needed for the experience (and no more).
- Follow up when you return to class (e.g., interpreting data, explaining findings).

(To think about teacher decision-making, turn to your Companion Manual and complete Textbook Activity 4.2)

Managing Ideas

In this textbook we have focused on the importance of science, technology, and society and the three instructional strategies that underlie these areas of study:

- Scientific inquiry.
- Technological problem-solving
- STS decision-making

Each instructional strategy helps children answer different types of questions arising from different kinds of problems, and leads to a characteristic solution result. To help you distinguish among the three contexts and their related strategies, examine Table 4.1.

Table 4.1

Characteristics of Instructional Strategies

Context	Scientific Inquiry	Technology	Science-Technology-Society (STS)
Instructional Strategy	Scientific inquiry	Technological problem-solving	STS decision-making
Type of Question	Why (does it happen)?	How (can we do it)?	Should (we do it)?
Source of Problem	Curiosity about phenomena in the natural world.	Human needs and wants.	Different perspectives on a science-related social issue.
Kind of Problem	Theoretical	Practical	Issue
Solution Result	Knowledge of the natural world.	A change in the manufactured world.	A defensible decision as to what to do about the issue.

Table 4.2 provides a sample problem and sample solution for each instructional strategy.

Table 4.2

Instructional Strategies: Sample Problems and Solutions

	Scientific Inquiry	Technological Problem-Solving	STS Decision–Making
Sample Problem	**Why** does my coffee cool so quickly?	**How** can I make a container to keep my coffee hot?	**Should** we use styrofoam cups or ceramic cups for our meeting?
Sample Explanation, Solution, or Action	Conduction, convection, and radiation transfer heat energy.	Styrofoam cups are manufactured to keep liquids hot for a period of time.	Some people have made the decision not to purchase hot drinks that are only served in styrofoam cups.

You may choose to teach entire units based on each instructional strategy, e.g., a scientific inquiry unit on *Hearing and Sound*, a technological problem-solving unit on *Mechanisms Using Electricity*, or an STS unit on *Waste and Our World*. You may also choose to incorporate more than one instructional strategy within a particular unit. For example, your *Hearing and Sound* unit may include an opportunity to build a musical instrument, which is technological problem-solving, or may include consideration of the problem of noise pollution, which is STS decision-making.

In order to manage ideas, teachers need to develop pedagogical content knowledge (PCK) (Shulman, 1986). PCK refers to the ability to integrate knowledge of content, curriculum, teaching, learning, and students to help students learn. Through experience and research teachers develop PCK specific to the teaching of various topics. For example, when teaching about the seasons, teachers with PCK would know some of the students' alternative conceptions such as the idea that the sun is closer to the earth in the winter than in the summer (an erroneous conception). When teaching about electricity teachers would know that many students think that a flashlight bulb in a simple electrical circuit "uses up" electricity and that there will be less electricity in the circuit after the bulb than before it, another erroneous conception. Further, the teacher would know that an empirical test using two ammeters placed at different locations in the circuit can provide evidence that contradicts the "using up" theory. When teaching technological problem-solving, teachers would know that many students think that technology only refers to large machines and computers, rather than to any object or device made by humans to fulfill a need.

Representing subject matter is a key aspect of pedagogical content knowledge. Experienced teachers do not just tell about science and technology but use their PCK to interpret it and transform it into forms that are accessible to students. One of the main kinds of representation in scientific inquiry and technological problem-solving is student activities. For example, instead of just telling her students about camouflage, a teacher sends them into the schoolyard to search for previously scattered colored toothpicks, then has them classify and total the number of each color found. Finding fewer green toothpicks than the other colors points students toward the idea of camouflage which the teacher then elaborates on through other examples and

activities. To give a technological problem-solving example, instead of just showing students pictures of different kinds of bridges, a teacher has them design and build a structure out of straws to span a gap of one metre. She then has them discuss the strengths and weaknesses of their bridge design. Through access to teaching resources and by reflecting on their own experience, teachers develop a repertoire of activities for each topic that they teach.

It is also important when teaching scientific inquiry to represent scientific explanations. Explanations are the goal of scientific inquiry but are both unfamiliar to students and removed from the world of direct experience (e.g., you can't see molecular spacing). To make the unfamiliar familiar and the invisible visible you can represent explanations using well-chosen metaphors, similes, analogies, and models.

- Metaphors are where a word or phrase that ordinarily designates one thing is used to designate another, making an implicit comparison between the two. For example: "The snail is a natural garbage collector."

- Similes make a comparison between two things using the words "like" or "as". For example, "The continents are like a giant jigsaw puzzle."

- Analogies are extended metaphors that point out similarities between seemingly unlike things, inferring that they might be alike in other ways as well. For example, "The circulatory system is to the body what a transportation system is to a country."

- Models are simplified representations of phenomena that suggest how they work. Physical models are actual devices or processes that behave like phenomena (e.g., a stream table models erosion and a balloon rocket models a space probe). Conceptual models use metaphors and analogies, (e.g., bouncing popcorn is a conceptual model for the atomic activity of gaseous particles).

Two General Teaching Approaches: Inductive and Deductive Teaching

A good place to start thinking about teaching strategies is to first consider two general overall approaches to teaching—inductive and deductive. All three instructional strategies of scientific inquiry, technological problem-solving, and STS decision-making can be approached more or less inductively or deductively. The inductive approach is more associated with the ideas of Bruner (e.g., discovery), while the deductive approach is more associated with the ideas of Ausubel (e.g., advance organizers) (See Chapter 2).

An inductive approach begins from particular examples and moves to a general principle that encompasses the examples. For example, students observe the characteristics of certain animals (e.g., beaver, rabbit, dolphin) with the intention that they will come to understand which features distinguish mammals from non-mammals. To give another example, students try making parachute canopies in various shapes (e.g., round, square, triangular) with the intention that they will come to understand which shape results in a more controlled descent.

A deductive approach begins with teaching a general principle and moves to particular examples that illustrate the principle. For example, students learn the general characteristics that help plants survive in a desert climate with the intention that they will use that knowledge and their observation skills to classify each member of a given set of plants as likely or unlikely to survive in the desert. To give another example, students learn through fair testing that triangles are a strong shape with the intention that they will use triangular bracing when they build model structures.

Both inductive and deductive approaches are appropriate in science and technology teaching. For example, having students enter into an activity with little knowledge of the relevant concepts lends an air of mystery to the learning which enhances motivation. On the other hand, providing students with important concepts in advance helps to focus their work and perhaps lead to more fruitful results. Most teachers mix inductive and deductive approaches.

Instruction in Scientific Inquiry

Essential Elements of Scientific Inquiry

Authentic instruction in scientific inquiry incorporates five essential elements that need to be kept in mind during teaching and learning. You should think of these elements as guidelines rather than as a recipe to be followed. The five elements are (NRC, 2000):

- Engaging with a scientific question or problem.

- Gathering evidence.

- Developing descriptions and explanations, based on the evidence.

- Evaluating explanations.

- Communicating with others regarding the inquiry and its results.

The five elements just described can also be thought of as the five phases of an instructional model called the Evidence-Explanation Model. You should keep in mind that the model is not linear but iterative and recursive and that the different phases interact with each other in many different ways.

Role of the Teacher

Scientific inquiry in schools is modeled after inquiry as carried out by scientists. However, students lack the level of understanding and ability of scientists and it would be unrealistic to leave them to inquire on their own. For successful classroom inquiry, teachers must play an active role throughout. *Scaffolding* is the term often used to describe teacher intervention, and means that the more knowledgeable teacher provides individualized support to student learning so that the learners can accomplish, with assistance, more than they could achieve alone (See Chapter 2 for previous discussion about scaffolding).

The amount of scaffolding needed varies during inquiry, depending on the abilities and experiences of the students. The nature of the intervention also varies on a continuum from teacher-directed to student-directed, depending on what the teacher and students judge is appropriate. As students proceed with their inquiries, you need to work out how you will address the following issues (NRC, 2000):

- Who or what is the source of the initial inquiry question? (e.g., Should I provide a single question? Should I provide a set of questions to select from? Should the students come up with a common question to investigate? Should each student come up with and investigate his own question?).

- What guidance do I provide while students gather evidence? (e.g., Should I tell students what evidence to collect and how and where to find it? Should the students decide what evidence they will collect and then figure out how to find and collect it?).

- What help do I give as students try to formulate descriptions and explanations? (e.g., To what degree should I be involved in pointing them towards significant patterns in their data? To what extent should I draw their attention to previous ideas that will help them explain what they are inquiring into now?).

- What assistance do I give to help students connect with scientific knowledge? (e.g., Should I point out the connections to scientific knowledge? Should I suggest where they might find the scientific knowledge? Should I let them research the question on their own?).

- To what degree should students take the lead in discussing their inquiry and its findings? (e.g., Should I provide all the groups with a procedure for their presentations? Should I give the groups some broad guidelines for their presentations? Should I let the groups decide on how they will organize their presentations?).

Intervening Through Questioning

Questioning is a very important type of intervention. Teacher questions stimulate student thinking and student responses provide feedback to the teacher about that thinking. Student questions provide clues about what they have learned. Experience will help you become adept at asking and encouraging good questions. Here are some guidelines to help you improve your questioning:

- Make questions as simple, unambiguous, and direct as possible. For example, a question such as "What about the seasons and Earth's orbital movement?" is ambiguous and could be restated as "How are the seasons influenced by the Earth's orbital movement?"

- Use a mixture of convergent (closed) questions, which have one or very few possible answers, and divergent (open) questions, which have many possible answers. For example, "How far did your vehicle travel?" is a convergent question while "Why do you think your vehicle turned to one side?" is a divergent question.

- Wait at least 3-5 seconds between posing the question and selecting a respondent. Two benefits of wait-time (Rowe, 1973) are that students can think more about an answer and more students have a chance to respond.

- Consciously listen to students, value what they say, and try to make sense of their responses. For example, when you respond with, "That's an interesting answer", you convey to the student that her idea is important.

- Probe students to get them to elaborate on and explain initial responses. For example, probes such as, "Why do you think so?" "Can you explain what you mean?" and "Can you give us an example?" encourage students to think more deeply.

Table 4.3

Science Questions Based on Bloom's Taxonomy.

Level	Definition	Sample Questions
Knowledge	Knowing specific facts and generalizations (e.g., by defining, describing, and listing).	What three animals are commonly found at a wetlands site?
		What happens to light when it strikes a smooth surface?
Comprehension	Understanding the meaning of what is learned (e.g., by classifying, summarizing, generalizing, and explaining).	What are two ways in which small animals avoid predators?
		What roles do worms have in the food chain?
Application	Applying previously learned knowledge to new situations (e.g., using, producing, transferring, and extending).	Why is this statement inaccurate: "Close the door you're letting in the cold"?
		How does temperature change affect us in our daily lives?
Analysis	Breaking down knowledge into its parts and trying to understand it (e.g., probing, examining, and investigating).	How can you use the evidence found at the crime scene to determine who is guilty?
		Using a hand lens, what similarities and differences among insects can you identify?
Synthesis	Putting knowledge together to make a new whole (e.g., generating, reconstructing designing, creating, and inventing).	What are some different ways that you could use two batteries and some wire to light a bulb?
		How could you test which form of insulation is better at keeping the water hot?
Evaluation	Judging the value of what is learned (e.g., appraising, interpreting, critiquing, and justifying).	If you retested mineral samples for hardness, how could you improve the accuracy of your tests?
		Why are trees and forests important to human society?

- Encourage students to listen to and value each other's questions and responses. For example, if you ask students to restate or comment on each other's answers they will attend more closely to what everyone else is saying.

- Teach students to ask good questions through teacher modeling and through a supportive classroom atmosphere that promotes participation. For example, help students by requesting them to ask questions beginning with words like "Why?" "How?" and "What if?"

We advise preservice and beginning teachers to write down questions as part of their lesson plans in order to allow time to think up good questions and provide guidance once they are in front of a class. As you gain experience you will be better able to generate appropriate questions as the lesson progresses. There are a variety of frameworks that can guide you in developing good questions, some of which are generic and apply to all subject areas. Table 4.3 gives some examples of science questions based on the six levels of Bloom's Taxonomy (1956).

Other useful questioning frameworks are subject-specific to science. Table 4.4 shows questions based on some of the skills described in Chapter 3.

Using Discrepant Events

One way to encourage students to question their existing ideas is to use a "discrepant event". The discrepancy is between what is expected and what actually happens. For example, students place a ball of paper towel in a drinking glass and push the glass top downward into a sink full of water. When they pull the glass straight up and out again they are surprised to find that the paper towel is still dry. The unexpected result raises feelings of curiosity and of wanting to know why, creating strong motivation for further investigation that can lead to new understanding, e.g., that air occupies space. Although it would be difficult to generate a discrepant event for

Table 4.4

Questions Based on Science Skills.

Observing	How does the pencil change in appearance when placed in water?
Measuring	Which ice cube melted the fastest?
Classifying	Why is a whale considered to be a mammal?
Communicating	How could you record your observations?
Inferring	What can we say about the relationship between the north poles of two magnets?
Generalizing	What can we conclude about the beak type of birds and the foods that they eat?
Explaining	How does the tilt of the earth's axis affect the seasons?
Predicting	Will the comb be attracted to the magnet? Why do you think so?
Formulating Models	How could you use the marbles and ruler to demonstrate a flow of electrical charge?
Experimenting	How could we find out if plant growth is affected by the amount of light?
Defining Operationally	How can we define carbon dioxide based on what we have just observed?
Formulating Hypotheses	How will adding soap affect the "stickiness" of the water?
Controlling Variables	Why do all the ice cubes have to be the same size at the beginning of the experiment?

every concept, many other discrepant events can be found in the accumulated science lore (Liem, 1987).

(To think more about scientific inquiry, turn to your Companion Manual and complete Textbook Activity 4.3)

Strategies for Teaching About the Nature of Science

Students need to develop an authentic notion of the nature of science (NOS) but there is no guarantee this will be accomplished simply by having them engage in scientific inquiry. For example, students will not necessarily gain a better understanding of the role of evidence in science just by finding evidence to support their explanations.

Teaching about the nature of science requires you to

- Decide on appropriate nature of science goals. For example, you may want students to understand that "Scientific explanations must be based on evidence."

- Meaningfully intertwine NOS goals about science with knowledge goals in science. For example, if you want students to understand that "Scientific explanations must be based on evidence" you must ensure that the explanations they develop during their inquiry are based on evidence.

- Make the NOS goals explicit to students during the lesson rather than hoping they will grasp them implicitly. For example, ask students to tell you the evidence their explanation is based on and point out how important this connection is in scientific inquiry.

Many important ideas about the nature of science can be taught within the context of scientific inquiry. Some key ideas and accompanying suggestions for teaching are:

- *While scientists agree generally on what constitutes a valid investigation, there is no fixed method or set of steps that they always follow.* Student groups compare and find differences in how they conducted the same investigation but also note similarities, e.g., each group tried to control the same variables.

- *Scientists use their senses and instruments to gather accurate data through observations and measurements in both natural settings and under controlled (laboratory) conditions.* Students provide examples of observations and measurements they have made, and the instruments they have used (e.g., microscope).

Students describe how a controlled investigation (e.g., testing leaves for chlorophyll) differs from an uncontrolled investigation (e.g., observing different shapes of leaves on trees in the same area).

- *Biases may influence the recording, interpreting, and reporting of scientific data.* Students give examples of experiences where they tried to explain away results that contradicted their existing ideas (e.g., suggesting that a combined mixture of 25 ml water and 25 ml methyl alcohol totaled only 48 ml due to a measuring error).

- *Scientific arguments must adhere to the principles of logical reasoning.* Students outline how their conclusions were inferred from the evidence that they gathered.

- *The validity of scientific claims is eventually resolved by referring back to observations of phenomena.* Students resolve a debate over the result of a test by repeating it (e.g., determining the hardness of a mineral by repeating the scratch test).

- *To be useful, a hypothesis should be testable and should suggest what evidence would support it and what evidence would refute it.* Students frame a hypothesis using an If…then… format so they can test it (e.g., If the mineral is a carbonate, then it will fizz when acid is dripped on it).

- *Scientific theories should be logically sound, incorporate a substantial body of valid observations, and use or be consistent with currently accepted scientific principles.* Students explain how their theory (e.g., their explanation for why a hot air balloon ascends to the ceiling of the room) meets the above three criteria

Strategies for Teaching About the History of Science

Teaching about the history of science can also help you achieve NOS goals. Current science textbooks necessarily present summaries of up-to-date scientific ideas, often without reference to their historical development. As a result, students may be left with the erroneous impression that scientific knowledge is a collection of facts that require little or no justification, undermining the critical importance of evidence and argument in scientific thinking. Because it shows how scientific ideas change over time, the history of science can help students gain a better understanding of "how we know" as well as "what we know".

Historical studies can show students the complex nature of the relationship between evidence and explanation. For example:

- The same evidence may be interpreted in different ways.
- Interpretations of particular evidence can change over time.
- Additional evidence may change previously held conclusions.

Studying the history of science is particularly useful in helping students better understand the nature of scientific theories. For example:

- The story of how Fleming came to realize the antibiotic properties of penicillin shows how scientific knowledge is generated by making observations and inventing theoretical explanations to make sense of them.
- The story of how the astronomer Leverrier used anomalies in Uranus' orbit to predict where to find the unknown planet Neptune shows how theories are validated by their predictive power.
- The story of how Wegener's idea of continental drift was rejected then later accepted shows that new scientific theories may encounter strong opposition in the short run but in the long run they are judged by their results.
- The story of how Darwin's theory of natural selection replaced Lamarck's theory of inheritance of acquired characteristics as the explanation for adaptation shows students that new theories are established in the place of previous theories when they explain more or answer more questions than their predecessors.

(To think about teaching the history and nature of science, turn to your Comapnion Manual and complete Textbook Activity 4.4)

Strategies for Connecting Science to Children's Everyday Lives

Science is not just an academic discipline but also helps us cope with everyday life. For example, science can help us understand what causes earthquakes or think intelligently about the implications of global warming. Further, students often have science-related questions based in their everyday experience, e.g., "How does a cat find its way in the dark?" "How do airplanes stay up in the air?" Introducing everyday applications of science into scientific inquiry can

- Enrich your teaching.
- Increase student motivation.
- Deepen student understanding.
- Show students that science is relevant to their lives.
- Encourage students to learn beyond the classroom.

You can use everyday applications both as a source of inquiry questions and as a way to help students consolidate what they have learned through their inquiries. Every science topic has many everyday applications (some of them connected to technology) that could be incorporated into teaching. Here are some examples, in the form of questions students might ask:

- *Senses*: How does a cat find its way in the dark? How does a hearing aid work?
- *Temperature:* Why is it cold in the winter? How does the stove burner get hot?
- *Rocks and Minerals:* Where do rocks come from? What is cement made out of?
- *Plant Growth and Changes:* How do plants get food? Why do some plants die?
- *Classroom Chemistry:* Why does peroxide fizz when my mother puts it on my cut? Why do cookies get bigger when you cook them?
- *Air and Aerodynamics:* Why is there wind? How does an airplane stay up in the air?

Instruction in Technological Problem-Solving

Essential Elements of Technological Problem-solving

Authentic instruction in technological problem-solving incorporates four essential elements.

- Identifying a design problem.
- Developing a design plan.
- Implementing the design plan.
- Evaluating the completed technological design or product.

The four elements just described can be thought of as the four phases of a model called the Technological Problem-Solving Model, where the phases overlap and connect in an iterative and recursive way.

Role of the Teacher

You must play an active role in technological problem-solving, just as in scientific inquiry. Again, this involves knowing when to step in and when to step back. In general, your interventions should:

- Be more directive at the start of the task and more supportive as the task progresses.

- Include questioning, reminding, cueing, focusing, and explaining.

- Challenge the students and affect the direction of their efforts in order to prevent frustration, extend achievement, and assess progress.

As students carry out design tasks, their thought processes and decision-making are exposed for all to see because the plans and models they create embody the development of their thinking. Because their thinking is concretized in their tasks, you can enhance their awareness of their design thinking by focusing them on the significance of what they are actually creating. You can have students reflect on their design tasks

- In verbal, written, and pictorial forms. For example, making sketches of three different alternative solutions to one design problem, then giving reasons for pursuing one rather than the other two.

- Through interaction with themselves, their peers, and the teacher. For example, looking at and discussing each other's design drawings.

- Before, during, and after the tasks are completed. For example, writing about a specific problem that was encountered and explaining how it was solved.

Your interventions should ensure that the interaction between the concrete expression of ideas through design (in the hands) and the development of design ideas (in the head) is an iterative process whereby thinking informs and advances doing and, simultaneously, doing informs and advances thinking. This will enable your students to strike a balance between active designing and reflective appraisal of the design. As the design work progresses, your interventions will help students:

- Examine chosen courses of action.

- Focus on decision points.

- Review decisions.

- Speculate on new directions of development.

- Evaluate results.

For example, you might assist students in understanding how and why they used bracing in their structure or how and why one proposed airplane wing design is superior to another.

Figure 4.1

Intervening Through Questioning in Technological Problem-Solving

Identifying a Design Problem	Why are you designing this product?
	What need will this product meet?
	What do you want to accomplish?
	What is your purpose?
	What are your requirements?
	Are there other factors you need to take into account?
	What materials do you have available and how can you use them?
Developing a Design Plan	What are some alternative solutions?
	Are there similar situations you might learn from?
	What are some general principles that might help you?
	What scientific knowledge might help you?
	How can you find out more?
	How can you put these ideas together to make them work?
	What is your plan?
Implementing the Design Plan	Is your plan working?
	How are you testing your plan?
	Which parts of your plan are working?
	Which parts of your plan are not working?
	How can you modify your plan?
	What alternatives do you have?
	What is your new plan?
	How well does your new plan work?
Evaluating the Completed Technological Design or Product	Does your design solution work?
	What steps did you follow?
	Was anything hard to do or understand?
	Is there anything you overlooked?
	How did your planning affect the product?
	Could you have planned in a different way?
	Could you solve this problem in a better way?
	What have you learned from this activity?

You should be aware that the design task itself will have a major effect on how your students approach and carry out the design work. The nature and setting of the task create context and meaning and provide starting points for student action. Further, the strictness of the constraints on the task (e.g., restrictions on dimensions or materials) has a major impact on how it can be done. More open-ended (ill-defined) tasks lend themselves to more alternative courses of action while more closed-ended (well-defined) tasks will have a narrower range of potential solution paths.

Intervening Through Questioning

While some questioning frameworks already presented in this chapter can provide useful guidelines for questioning in all contexts, they are most relevant to scientific inquiry. You should also be aware of the types of questions that are more specific to technological problem-solving, where the main purpose is to get students to reflect on the tasks they are doing and how and why they are doing them.

Figure 4.1 gives examples of questions that are appropriate during the different phases of technological problem-solving and relate to the particular aspects of design that correlate with those phases. However, the questions may also overlap with other phases:

(To think about science and technology teaching strategies, turn to your Companion Manual and complete Textbook Activity 4.5)

Strategies for Teaching About Drawing in Design

You should incorporate design drawing into all stages of your students' design work because designers rely heavily on drawing and view it as both a common language and a concrete mode of thought. Design drawing is a tool for thinking and has two overlapping roles: representing ideas and generating ideas. Representational drawings show a marked similarity with what is being depicted and their main purpose is to portray what exists (e.g., a final drawing of the finished product). Generative drawings are more ambiguous and are used to produce, develop, and extend ideas. Generative drawings are especially important at the beginning of a design project and are epitomized in the initial freehand sketches that propose a broad design direction and allow for subsequent exploration of ideas.

You can emulate how designers use different kinds of representational and generative drawings by having students draw before, during, and at the end of their work. First, prior to embarking on a specific project, students can fill small sketchbooks with drawings of a wide range of subjects (e.g., kitchen devices, bridges, buildings, vehicles) augmented by written notes and reflections. This will record essentials and impressions

for later use and inspire future projects. Once their design project begins, students need to create three kinds of drawings: beginning sketches, elaborating and refining drawings, and final presentation drawings.

- Beginning sketches made at the start of the project indicate students' initial thoughts and key ideas. They should be exploratory and conceptual rather than representational, and made quickly and spontaneously. They should include both images and words.

- As the design work progresses, students should continue creating various elaborating and refining drawings, both freehand and hard-line (ruler drawn), to share with other design team members. These drawings, which should show increasing accuracy and detail, will help transform, expand, and develop ideas expressed in initial sketches. This process of thinking through drawing has been referred to as visual thinking (Arnheim, 1967).

- At the end of the project, students should make a final presentation drawing that is a recognizable representation of the finished design. It should be hard-line, finished, precise, detailed, labeled, and even measured. People outside the design process should theoretically be able to use it as an accurate guide to making. When working with children you can have each student group build another group's design using the other group's presentation drawing.

Strategies for Teaching About the Nature of Technology

It is just as important to improve students' understanding of the nature of technology (NOT) as it is to improve their understanding of the nature of science. Further, there is no guarantee this will be accomplished simply by having them engage in technological problem-solving. Similar to the nature of science, teaching about the nature of technology requires you to

- Decide on appropriate nature of technology goals. For example, you may want student to understand that "Designs require testing."

- Meaningfully intertwine NOT goals about technology with knowledge goals in technology. For example, if you want students to understand that "Designs require testing" you must ensure that they test their designs.

- Make the NOT goals explicit to students during the lesson rather than hoping they will grasp them implicitly. For example, ask students to tell you what their tests revealed and point out to them why technological designs need to get tested.

Many important ideas about the nature of technology relate to doing technological problem-solving and can be taught in that context. Some key ideas and accompanying suggestions for teaching are:

- *Design is always constrained by physical laws.* Students explain how the design of their boat is constrained by the requirement that the boat must float, or how the design of their electric buzzer is constrained by the requirement that the buzzer will only work if the electrical circuit is complete.

- *Design is constrained by flexible factors (e.g., user-friendliness, aesthetics, economics, politics, respect for the environment).* Students explain how the design of their straw towers is constrained by the requirement that they build it from a certain maximum number of straws (economics).

- *Every design problem has many alternative potential solutions depending on the values placed on various constraints.* Students discuss how they balanced the requirement that their model car travel a certain distance with the requirement that it have an attractive design.

- *An optimum design considers all constraints and strikes a reasonable compromise to reach an elegant solution.* Students debate whether any vehicle they design can maximize all constraints, i.e., simultaneously be the safest, most efficient, least expensive, and the most beautiful.

- *Designs require testing, especially when they are unusual, complex, or costly.* Students suggest how they can test their boat to see how well it floats.

- *Over–design and redundancy are hedges against failure.* Students discuss how the test of their bridge shows it holds more than the required weight and explain why they designed it to be stronger than calculated requirements.

Using examples and mini case studies from current and past technology can also help you achieve NOT goals. For example:

- Studying the design of a very tall structure such as the Manulife Building in Edmonton shows the many ways in which building design operates within the constraint of gravity.

- Studying and choosing among the different designs that several architects propose for the same building (e.g., a new art gallery) shows how every design problem has many alternative potential solutions.

- Studying sample sketches from the notebooks of professional designers shows how design requires creativity and innovation.

- Studying the school heating system (get the custodian to help!) shows how technological systems require human and non-human controls (e.g., meters, switches), as well as how control involves comparing information (feedback) about what is happening with information about what is supposed to happen and making required adjustments.

- Studying the historical changes in how music is recorded (e.g., vinyl records, eight-track tapes, cassette tapes, CDs, and DVDs) can show how decisions about technology are influenced by many social factors (e.g., consumer acceptance, cost, and economic competition).

- Studying the many effects of the automobile on society can show how technology has influenced large-scale social changes (e.g., service stations, freeways, fast food outlets, and suburban shopping malls).

Strategies for Connecting Technology to Children's Lives

Students are much more aware of the everyday applications of technological problem-solving than the applications of scientific inquiry because students live primarily in a manufactured world and the products of technology are integral to their lives (e.g., books, clothes, toys, video games, computers, and bicycles). Outside of school, children also participate in technological problem-solving (e.g., building objects and devices from kit materials, and taking apart already existing objects and devices and [sometimes!] putting them back together).

As already noted, you can use everyday applications of technology to teach students about the nature of technology. You can also use everyday applications to teach students about the connections between science and technology. Here, in the form of questions, are some examples:

- How does a pair of glasses help you see better?
- How does a thermometer work?
- How do your brakes slow down and stop your bicycle?
- How does a toy that has an electric motor in it work?
- How is playground equipment built to be strong and stable?

(To think about technological design, turn to your Companion Manual and complete Textbook Activity 4.6)

Instruction in STS Decision-Making

Elements of STS Decision-Making

Authentic instruction in STS decision-making incorporates six essential elements. You should think of these elements as guidelines rather than as a recipe to be followed. The six elements are

- Understanding the issue.
- Identifying alternative courses of action.
- Investigating perspectives and consequences of actions.
- Deciding on a course of action.
- Taking action.
- Evaluating actions and decision-making.

The six elements just described can be thought of as the six phases of a model called the STS Decision-Making Model, where the phases overlap and connect in an iterative and recursive way.

Keeping the Science in STS

During STS decision-making, students think about what scientific and technological knowledge might help lead to a decision as to what action to take. One danger of STS decision-making is that the science may be lost due to a focus on the social, political, economic, and other factors. But the science is an essential aspect of the practical reasoning required to reach a defensible decision about what action to take about the issue. For example, there is a great deal of scientific knowledge related to deciding whether or not to close a hazardous waste plant that incinerates polychlorobiphenyls (PCBs), including knowledge about combustion, soils, water systems, food chains, and overall, the effects of PCBs and products of PCB incineration on living organisms. Understanding the science is necessary if it is to play a role in informing (but not exclusively determining) the decision-making.

Controversy and STS

You should be aware that STS issues can be controversial. Disputes about the validity of any claims, including those that appear to have the support of the scientific community, are typical of STS and developing students' abilities to assess these claims is of critical importance.

There are two main reasons for controversy. First, an issue typically involves different competing interests or stakeholders. For example, a private corporation, the government, the townspeople, company employees, First Nations, Metis, and Inuit, and the general public might all have a stake in whether or not to close a hazardous waste plant. Second, there will likely be disagreement among stakeholders even regarding the science knowledge claims (e.g., how they bear on the issue and how much weight they should be given when making a decision). For example, there may be agreement that a waste plant is emitting ash into the air but there may also be sharp disagreement among identified experts on whether the emissions involve any risk to health or to the environment. Disagreement about how to interpret the science can occur because:

- Different stakeholders have different interests relating to the issue, e.g., profit vs. pollution, and those interests can influence how they interpret scientific reports.

- There may be insufficient scientific knowledge relating to the issue, causing people to place various interpretations on personal knowledge brought to bear on the issue.

It is important to help students critically scrutinize any claims relating to STS issues, including the scientific claims. This is an aspect of scientific literacy and requires looking carefully at the evidence, both scientific and anecdotal, including how it was gathered and how it might bear on the issue. Often, the decision as to which position an individual takes on an STS issue comes down to which scientific expert they agree with, which in turn may depend largely on the individual's existing beliefs. For teachers, this highlights the need to develop students' critical thinking skills so that they base their decisions on a thoughtful consideration of evidence and reasons (see Chapter 1 for more discussion about scientific literacy).

Taking Action

STS teaching includes taking action. Taking action is the logical result of coming to a reasoned decision about an issue, even though it is easier to state that one cares about an issue than to do something about it. In the context of the classroom, the question of how to take action requires very careful consideration. The first consideration involves the kinds of actions that might be considered acceptable for students to participate in. Suitable actions relating to environmental issues, for example, might include conducting surveys, making public statements, writing letters, organizing petitions, publishing newsletters, working on environmental clean-up projects, and assuming responsibility for environmental enhancement of the school grounds, or just taking personal actions such as turning off the tap during teeth brushing.

The second consideration is more subtle because it concerns the actual effect of the action. The most thoughtful actions carried out with the best motives may not actually influence how any particular issue is eventually resolved or not resolved. This may lead students to the pessimistic conclusion that participating in STS decision-making and taking action are rather pointless endeavors. As a teacher, it is important that you try to help students gain a better understanding of how decisions are made and where the power of decision-making is located. You may also wish to discuss the important difference between the students influencing the decision-makers and the students actually becoming the decision-makers.

(To think about STS decision-making, turn to your Companion Manual and complete Textbook Activity 4.7)

Other Strategies

General Teaching Strategies

Each of the three contexts of science teaching–science, technology, and STS–are linked to a particular instructional strategy–scientific inquiry, technological problem-solving, and STS decision-making. There are also many other general teaching strategies that can be used in any context. You can improve your effectiveness by becoming adept at incorporating these into your repertoire. Additional strategies include:

- **Socratic Dialogue:** Socratic dialogue emulates the teaching method of the Greek philosopher Socrates. Based on the assumption that most people know more than they think they do, it involves using well thought out questioning to bring to the surface what students may not be aware that they already know.

- **Demonstrations:** Teacher demonstrations are useful when potential student science activities are constrained by factors such as lack of time, lack of materials and equipment, deficiencies in manipulative skills, and safety considerations.

- **Direct Teaching (Exposition):** Direct teaching can present a quantity of science content in a structured fashion to a large group of students in a minimum of time. Digital and non-digital media can make the presentation more compelling.

- **Games:** You can use games–including hands on, mental, outdoor, and online games—to teach science. Games can be student-made, teacher-made, or commercial. Truly useful games build student understanding rather than accumulate isolated facts.

- **Simulations:** A variety of scientific simulations are available on the World Wide Web. Simulations display things that you can not see (e.g., molecules, genes) or present physical situations difficult to illustrate in the classroom context (e.g., food chains). Simulations may include opportunities for students to interact with the simulation (e.g., by changing one variable and observing the effect).

- **Role Playing:** Role playing helps to place science and technology in context and can help students develop knowledge, skills, and attitudes. Students are motivated by the opportunity to use their imaginations (e.g., they can role-play forensic scientists and use fingerprinting, chromatography, and other evidence to catch an imaginary thief).

- **Problem-solving:** The setting of problems by teachers or students and their solution fits well into scientific inquiry, technological problem-solving, and STS decision-making. Carefully thought-out problems provoke student thinking and can also help evaluate student understanding (e.g., "How could you build an unsinkable boat?").

- **Product Testing:** Household products provide opportunities for students to devise and carry out controlled experimental tests, as well as engage in STS decision-making. For example, students could test three different kinds of paper towels to determine which are the most absorbent and the best buy for the money.

- **Analyzing Case Studies:** A case study is a detailed description of an event, situation, issue, institution, or person (e.g., discovery of penicillin, cloning of an animal, invention of the laser). Analysis of cases can facilitate an understanding of scientific knowledge and inquiry, the nature of science, technological problem-solving, and STS decision-making.

- **Independent Projects:** Projects such as collections, experiments, inventions, and reports allow students to exercise more independence and responsibility for their own learning. They can try their own ideas and study what is of real interest to them, which builds intrinsic interest. Projects still require teacher guidance, monitoring, feedback, and support.

- **Research Projects:** An extended research project allows students to synthesize their understanding of a range of ideas. This also conveys how research is integral to what scientists and technologists do.

- **Presentations:** Student presentations provide empowering opportunities for students to integrate and summarize their learning into a form that is understandable by others. Presentations improve written and oral skills, as well as provide opportunities for other students to think critically.

Computers

Computers are increasingly being integrated into instruction and can be used in various ways:

- **Word Processing:** Students can use computers for writing science reports.

- **Graphics programs:** Students can draw models they intend to build.

- **Networks:** Students can communicate with the instructor and other students to ask questions, propose ideas, and comment on the ideas of others.

- **Tutorials:** Students can learn the content and skills of science and technology by accessing text, diagrams, animations, and audio and video, as well as link to relevant activities that apply what they learn.

- **Databases:** Students can access well-organized, electronically filed information about specific science, technology, and STS topics.

- **Research:** Students can use a variety of online sources to do extended, in-depth research on science, technology, and STS topics.

- **Simulations:** Students can view and interact with models of phenomena and events they cannot directly experience (e.g., human heart, waste processing plant).

- **Games:** Students can play online games related to topics that educate them about science and technology.

Like any other instructional tool, computers have their pros and cons. Pros of using computers include:

- High level of student interest.

- Immediate feedback to student responses.

- Learners can progress at their own rates.

- Instruction can be individualized.

- Students can gain access to inaccessible phenomena (e.g., through simulations).

Cons of computers include:

- Students must take time to learn new skills.

- Equipment and software are expensive.

- Computer-related activities vary in value.

- Less time for hands-on activities.

- Less time for face-to-face interaction with teacher and peers.

Integrating Science and Technology With Other Subjects

Integrating science meaningfully with other subjects such as language arts has at least three main benefits:

- Provides more contexts in which to think about science and technology.

- Shows how knowledge is interconnected.

- Provides increased time to teach science and technology.

The major danger of integration is that the science and technology will be subsumed into other subject areas to the point where they become unrecognizable. For example, in mathematics, just using displacement of water to find the volume of irregular solids will not teach students about the science of why objects float unless you address the latter goal specifically. As a teacher, you should always keep in mind the characteristics of science and technology and ensure that they are retained even when you are integrating science and technology with other subject areas.

Summary Ideas

This chapter presents some current thinking about:

- *What teaching is and how it relates to learning.* Teaching can be defined as an interactive manner that respects the thinking and ideas of those being taught. The teaching-learning relationship is indirect and is affected by many factors.

- *Managing students.* Classroom management is essential to effective teaching. Teachers can draw on ideas from a number of different management systems to help them make their classes run smoothly and productively.

- *Scientific inquiry.* Scientific inquiry is the recommended instructional strategy for science. A current view of classroom inquiry focuses around engaging with a question, gathering evidence, explaining, evaluating explanations including in light of current scientific knowledge, and communicating results.

- *Technological problem-solving.* Technological problem-solving is the recommended instructional strategy for teaching technology. A current view of classroom problem-solving focuses around identifying a technological problem, developing a plan for solution, implementing the plan, and evaluating the completed product or design.

- *STS decision-making.* STS decision-making is the recommended instructional strategy for teaching science-technology-society. A current view of classroom decision-making focuses around understanding the issue, identifying alternative courses of action, investigating perspectives and consequences of actions, deciding on a course of action, taking action, and evaluating actions and decision-making.

- *Other teaching strategies.* There are many general teaching strategies available that can be used within scientific inquiry, technological problem-solving, and STS decision-making. Examples include case study analysis, field experiences, problem-solving, and computers.

Making Productive Connections

Scenario 1

You have just been hired as an elementary teacher. Your principal asks you to plan a unit on waste that incorporates all three of scientific inquiry, technological-problem-solving, and STS decision-making. Create a unit plan of eleven lessons, based on the SLEs in the *Waste and Our World* unit of the *Alberta Elementary Science Program of Studies* (1996), that fulfils the conditions set by your principal.

Scenario 2

Book

In *Engineering Design Methods* (Cross, 1989), Nigel Cross points out that in professional design, "A related part of the complexity of modern design is the need to develop team work, with many specialists collaborating in and contributing to the design" (p. 31). How would you go about developing teamwork in technological problem-solving in your classroom? Keeping in mind that Cross is referring to professional designers, do you

think that developing teamwork is an appropriate goal for science classrooms? Why or why not?

Ideas to Think About When Teaching Science, Technology, and Society

- How well am I balancing my interventions with independent student work?
- How is my teaching using and conveying an authentic image of scientific inquiry?
- How am I using and conveying an authentic image of technological problem-solving?
- How am I using and conveying an authentic image of STS decision-making?
- How am I am using a variety of instructional strategies?
- How am I integrating my classroom management with my learning goals?

Selected Readings

Ayers, H., Gray, F. (1998). *Classroom Management: A Practical Approach for Primary and Secondary Teachers.* London: D. Fulton.

This book provides helpful advice on managing classrooms.

Eggleston, J. (1996). *Teaching Design and Technology (2nd edition).* Buckingham, UK: Open University Press.

This book is an excellent guide to the theory and practice of teaching technological problem-solving.

Harlen, W. (2000). *Teaching, Learning and Assessing Science 5-12* (3rd ed.). London: Paul Chapman.

This science methods text provides many helpful insights into teaching.

National Research Council (2000). *Inquiry and the National Education Standards.* Washington DC: National Academy Press.

This book, based on the U.S. National Science Education Standards, provides a detailed description of what it means to implement scientific inquiry in the classroom.

Solomon, J., & Aikenhead, G. (Eds.) (1992). *STS Education: International Perspectives on Reform.* New York: Teachers College.

This book presents the perspectives of various authors on the teaching of STS.

Selected Websites

BLOOMSBURG UNIVERSITY, PENNSYLVANIA

http://departments.bloomu.edu/scienced/inquiry.htm

This website provides links to a variety of resources on scientific inquiry and the nature of science.

THE LIGHTHOUSE FOR EDUCATION SITE: DESIGN TECHNOLOGY

http://tlfe.org.uk/designtechnology.htm

This British website provides support and links relating to technological problem-solving.

NSTA POSITION STATEMENT ON STS

http://www.nsta.org/159&psid=34

This statement by the National Science Teachers Association concisely sums up the STS approach to science teaching.

THE REALLY BIG LIST OF CLASSROOM MANAGEMENT RESOURCES: DR. BILL MARTIN

http://drwilliampmartin.tripod.com/classm.html

This website includes a list of over 400 resources for classroom management.

SCIENCE GAMES ONLINE

http://childparenting.about.com/od/sciencegamesonline

This website provides a lengthy list of games suitable for teaching science.

SCIENCE LEARNING NETWORK (SLN)

http://www.sln.org/resources/

This website provides links to a variety of web-based scientific inquiry projects.

UNIVERSITY OF OREGON WESTERN REGIONAL RESOURCE CENTER: INSTRUCTIONAL STRATEGIES

http://interact.uoregon.edu/wrrc/InstStrat.htm

This website provides links to a number of internet sites that provide useful information about teaching strategies.

Chapter 5
Planning to Teach STS

Learning Objectives

In this chapter, you should learn

- Why planning is important.
- What guidelines teachers should follow when preparing to teach.
- How to write long-range and short-range plans.
- How scientific inquiry, technological problem-solving, and STS decision-making plans differ.

Thinking About Your Existing Ideas

Write down your answers to the following questions. After you complete this chapter, revisit your answers. Which of your ideas remained the same and which changed? How did they change, and what do you believe caused the changes?

- Why do you think teachers spend time planning?
- What do teachers need to know in order to plan?
- What kinds of plans do teachers need?
- What information should be in these different kinds of plans?

Important Planning Ideas

During student teaching experiences, preservice teachers are expected to write plans and then use those plans to teach students. When we ask preservice teachers to describe these student teaching planning experiences they report that:

- Frequently they had to write plans during their evenings and weekends.
- It was challenging to create motivating science and technology lessons that would capture their students' interests.
- It was difficult to locate teaching resources that contained good ideas.
- Sometimes they had to write lessons plans while other times they had to design an entire unit of plans.
- Plans did not always turn out the way they had intended.
- At the end of the lesson, it was difficult to know what the students had really learned.

These responses reveal preservice teachers' concerns about doing a good job, their insights into the complexities of planning for teaching, and their general observations of the profession. Overall, they indicate just some of the challenges faced by all teachers who care about helping students develop an understanding and appreciation of science, technology, and society.

In order to plan for teaching, you need to consider many of the ideas presented so far in this textbook and connect these to ideas still to be presented in Chapter 6. In Chapter 1, you considered ideas about scientific and technological literacy and the nature of science and technology. Your beliefs about what science and technology are and how they happen should influence your plans and during your lessons, the words you use to describe science and technology.

In Chapter 2, you read about how children learn and what influences their understanding of scientific and technological concepts. Ideas about children's alternative conceptions and the role they play in influencing understanding, should lead to plans that allow time to survey these ideas and discuss their implications with the children. Messages about the time needed to consider a new idea and perhaps change an existing perception, and the importance of helping students make productive connections between ideas, should influence you to allow time in your plans to revisit the same concept within a number of different contexts.

Chapter 3 emphasized the importance of concepts, skills, and attitudes. All three of these components should appear in plans you write throughout the school year.

Chapters 3 and 4 emphasized the importance of scientific inquiry, technological problem-solving, and STS decision-making. A scientific inquiry instructional strategy asks students to explore questions that are personally meaningful, make observations, record data, and evaluate results. A technological problem-solving instructional strategy asks students to identify a problem, design a solution, implement the solution, and evaluate the design or product. A STS decision-making instructional strategy asks students to gather information about an issue, identify alternatives, investigate consequences, decide on a course of action, and evaluate those actions. A teacher's belief in the importance of these instructional strategies should influence lesson plan format and the selection of teaching strategies and activities.

Chapter 4 introduced you to a variety of teaching strategies to keep in mind as you think about teaching children in classrooms. Decisions about how to begin lesson, how to engage children in the lesson, and how to assess what children have learned all influence the format and content of your plans.

An additional consideration when planning is the assessment strategies that you will use with children. In Chapter 6, you will have the opportunity to think about the variety of assessment strategies that you can use in your plans to help answer the challenging question "What did my students learn?" (To think about your planning during student teaching, turn to your Companion Manual and do Textbook Activity 5.1.)

Why Planning is Important

When we talk about planning with our preservice teachers, sometimes they ask whether it really is necessary to spend time writing plans. They argue that their time is better spent working with the children. Also, they say that plans can easily be stored in their memories and do not necessarily need to be written down. These arguments show that our preservice teachers are still grappling with the issues of why planning is important and why they should devote time to keeping written records.

Probably the most important reason for writing plans is that this practice is a critical component of effective teaching. Writing plans and then thinking about how to improve those plans helps you to become a reflective decision-maker. Keeping written records of what you have taught and what could be done differently next time encourages a thoughtful approach to teaching and supports your professional growth. Taking time to create written plans also allows you to create a pedagogical record of how you worked to meet provincial standards. Written plans, therefore, provide you with a record of your original plans, revisions to those plans, and reflections on how to change the plans for next year.

Other important reasons for writing plans relate to working within the school context. For example, written plans provide supply teachers with guidance if you are absent, plans written by beginning teachers are frequently monitored by school administrators, and plans can become a component of your teaching evaluations. Furthermore, written records are needed in order to report to parents about the scope and nature of your program.

Writing plans, therefore, helps you to become a more effective teacher who is knowledgeable about learners, curriculum, resources, and pedagogy and is able to reflect on the decisions underlying planning choices. Written plans provide a record to others interested in evaluating your teaching abilities or understanding the scope of your program.

Planning for Scientific Inquiry

Before beginning to locate teaching resources or consider the kinds of plans you need to write, you should take the time to think about your future classroom. What pictures come to mind when you think about your students and what they should be doing during science class? What do you imagine your role might be? What do you want to accomplish by teaching science, technology, and society to students? These questions, and others, can lead to thinking about scientific inquiry, the forms it may take, and its place in your future classroom.

In Chapter 3, scientific inquiry was defined as a process of seeking answers to questions and some myths about scientific inquiry were presented. In classrooms, inquiry lessons usually begin with a question, encourage students to research information and undertake an investigation or experiment, involve making observations, and then conclude with evaluating data.

Although inquiry should be happening in many of your science classes, you should realize that inquiry takes many forms. For example, inquiry can be highly structured where you have selected questions for the students' investigations and have some very definite goals in mind. Inquiry can also be quite open-ended where students are exploring a number of materials and then generating their own questions for future investigation. Either interpretation of inquiry is acceptable; your choice of teaching strategies depends on what you are trying to help the students understand on any particular day.

Inquiry lessons should encompass a variety of teaching strategies. What this means for your classroom is that you should plan to use a variety of different teaching strategies (e.g., such as reading and writing) to help your students construct an understanding of science. (To get a sense of what is involved in balancing students' interests with a mandated curriculum, go to the Companion Manual and do Textbook Activity 5.2.)

Planning for Technological Problem Solving

You should also take time to think about what your class may look like when you teach technological problem solving. What do you see yourself doing during these lessons? What will the students be doing? How will you know if your students are learning concepts, skills, and attitudes? These questions lead to thinking about what technological problem-solving is and why it is viewed as an important component of school programs.

In Chapter 3, you read that technological problem-solving included skills such as designing, planning, making, troubleshooting, evaluating, and communicating. Similar to the skills associated with scientific inquiry, these technological problem-solving skills could not be separated from content or context. When you plan technological problem- solving lessons, therefore, you must vary the subject matter of the lessons to encourage students to practice these skills in a variety of contexts.

You also need to be aware of the kinds of knowledge that should be developed by students through their participation in technological problem-solving. For example, students need opportunities to develop procedural, conceptual, and strategic knowledge. Your plans, therefore, should include teaching strategies for helping students to construct these kinds of knowledge.

Technological problem-solving plans should account for the recursive or iterative thinking that characterizes technological thinking. Solving technological problems is not straightforward. Your lessons should allow students to follow a variety of paths to solving technological problems. For example, some of your lessons may simply involve discussing ongoing problems with the whole class. During these lessons, students can use manipulatives to illustrate their difficulties while other students offer potential solutions. Other lessons may involve the children in searching the Internet for background technical information related to their classroom projects. On other days, the students may be drawing plans or creating blueprints for their proposed product or device. Technological problem-solving, therefore, involves a variety of teaching strategies and all are needed in order to be sensitive to the diversity of students in your classroom and to accurately reflect how technological problems are solved.

Planning for STS Decision-Making

In Chapter 3, you read that STS decision-making involves the consideration of science and technology-related social issues with the intention of addressing the question "Should we do this?" What will lessons that revolve around this question look like? What kinds of investigations and discussions will the students be doing? How will you integrate concepts, skills, and attitudes into these lessons?

When planning to incorporate science, technology, and society into your teaching units, you need to think about how you can achieve a *balance* between these kinds of lessons and how you can assist children to gain a *balanced view* of STS issues. Some teachers plan to incorporate STS decision-making into all lessons within a unit. For example, a scientific inquiry lesson about batteries and bulbs can also include discussion about alternative forms of energy and the decision-making that underpins the energy choices we make. A technological problem-solving lesson about building objects that can serve as containers can also include discussion about the choices made when purchasing products that may or may not be packaged in recyclable materials.

Other teachers may plan STS decision-making lessons that are linked to other lessons in the unit, but are more extensive in their scope. For example, a unit on trees and forests may include extensive study of the impact of humans on forest habitats, the factors behind the choices we make, alternative ways of viewing forests, and the consequences of each alternative course of action.

STS decision-making plans, therefore, involve a variety of approaches to planning and all are needed in order to address the variety of topics in science programs, show sensitivity to the community in which you are teaching, and assist students to understand the importance of their personal choices.

General Guidelines for Preparing to Plan

Although you will be teaching a range of concepts, skills, and attitudes and using a variety of teaching strategies, as you begin to plan you will likely follow a similar pattern of *planful thinking*. Some general guidelines many effective teachers follow when planning any lesson include the following:

- *Decide what you are going to teach.* You need to consult your local curriculum for guidelines about appropriate topics, and then select specific concepts, skills, and attitudes to be developed in each lesson. Ask yourself: Do I know provincial curriculum expectations? How will I link my students' interests with curriculum expectations?

- *Think about what you know about the topic.* You need to consider your own understanding of the topic. Ask yourself: Do I understand the science and technology concepts for this lesson? Do I know what makes some concepts difficult to understand? Do I understand how concepts interconnect with each other? Do I understand the concepts that can be used to link lessons to other lessons and units?

- *Think about the students you will be teaching.* You need to find out what your students already know about the topic by surveying your students, reading the range of ideas written in their notebooks, or consulting the research literature. You also need to think about the abilities and backgrounds of your students. Ask yourself: Do I know the alternative conceptions and the useful ideas students have that are related to the topic? How can I balance students' interests with a mandated program? How can I adapt my lesson so all my students can grow in understanding and achieve success?

- *Find out what resources can assist with the lesson.* You need to locate a variety of teaching resources that can provide background information and useful activity ideas (e.g., Internet sites, materials kits, print resources, software, and CDs). Ask yourself: Do I know what criteria to use in order to select and evaluate good teaching resources? (See Appendix A for ideas about handling and storing materials safely. See Appendix B for guidelines about using living organisms in the classroom. See Appendix C for ideas about purchasing classroom resources. See Appendix D for ideas about how to select good teaching resources and locate the list of recommended resources for Alberta.)

- *Think about the teaching strategies you will use.* You need to consider how you can use a variety of teaching strategies to enhance students' learning. Ask yourself: How will I help students link this lesson to other lessons? How will I engage students in thinking about the present lesson? What will I do at the beginning, middle, and conclusion of the lesson?

- *Think about how you will assess students' learning.* You need to think about how to keep records of the students' thinking and understanding. Ask yourself: What will indicate to me that the students have grown towards understanding concepts and developing skills and attitudes?

An assumption underlying the above guidelines is that what the students eventually learn is identical to what in the local curriculum. This is not necessarily the case. Schmidt (1996) identifies three major dimensions of curriculum: the intended curriculum (e.g., goals found in curriculum documents), the implemented curriculum (e.g., the teacher's instructional strategies and choice of activity), and the attained curriculum (e.g., what the students actually achieve and understand through their educational experiences). For example, a curriculum document may include the goal that children should learn about how soil is formed. One teacher could read this goal and proceed to plan a lesson in which students search Internet sites to find out the range of factors that result in soil formation. Another teacher could decide that the most important idea about soil formation is the notion of time. His students might explore why areas of the world have different soil depths and fertility and the influence this has had over time on local agricultural practices. Yet another teacher may have her children examine soils taken from several local areas and classify the constituents that comprise those soils. Students could then speculate on parent materials and consult local geological surveys. In each case, the teacher began with reading the intended curriculum, but then diverged to implement the curriculum in a variety of ways. The

attained curriculum would be different in each class as it would be influenced by the teacher's thinking, the ideas brought to the lesson, the directions taken during discussions, and the conclusions achieved.

Another important idea about planning is that lesson plans suggest a linear sequence that may not resemble what actually takes place. For example, written lesson plans usually begin with an objective or a lesson intent, then proceed to detail the lesson introduction, development, and conclusion. But a lesson plan is only a logical prediction of how the teacher thinks the lesson will happen. Teaching is inherently uncertain–no lesson ever happens exactly as planned. Instead, a lesson plan should be thought of as a scaffold on which to hang the lesson rather than a recipe to be followed. During a lesson, you must be constantly aware of how the students are responding to the lesson and this may lead to changing aspects of the lesson "on the fly". For example, during lessons teachers constantly gather and interpret feedback from students through asking questions and getting responses, and by circulating among students and observing what they are doing. Students' responses may show that they have found some aspect of the plan to be unmanageable, too difficult, or completely mystifying. Teachers can then slightly alter the lesson (e.g., suggesting a new way of handling the equipment), or make a more profound change (e.g., altering the lesson intent or discussion to address what the students found intriguing). In some cases, the lesson may need to be abandoned altogether (e.g., an unanticipated safety issue emerged that showed the lesson needed to be completely rethought). Regardless, lesson plans and their apparent logical sequences represent your best judgment at the time. In the reality of the classroom, expect to encounter events and ideas that may lead to an alternative lesson emphasis, a change in instructional strategies, or even a complete rethinking of the lesson.

Long-Range and Short-Range Plans

Effective teachers use a combination of long–range and short–range plans to describe how they intend to implement curriculum expectations. Year plans are long–range plans that you create for each subject you teach. Year plans provide you with an outline of what you will be teaching during the school year.

Short–range plans take the form of unit plans, lessons plans, and daily plan books. Unit plans are written for each topic or unit that you have listed in your year plan.

For example, in your year plan you may plan to teach topics such as *Light and Shadows, Plant Growth and Changes, Wheels and Levers, Waste and Our World and Building Devices and Vehicles That Move.* Each of these topics would then be developed into a unit plan that provides more specific information about your intentions for the unit. Lesson plans are written for each lesson you teach. Some lessons may span several classes because of the time involved in introducing the topic, completing the activity, or reflecting on the learning (e.g., a lesson involving building bridges using a variety of materials may take several days). A daily plan book is a useful summary to keep of events and happenings in your classroom and gives you a quick reference you can use when talking with parents and students.

In your curriculum and instruction classes, you will likely be introduced to different approaches to planning, and to different formats for plans. You should, however, be able to identify some general trends in how teachers plan. Your responsibility is to recognize these trends, incorporate these ideas into your personal philosophy, and eventually generate your own approach to planning.

Year Plans

Schools require teachers to make plans that span an entire school year. At the beginning of the school year, principals frequently ask to view teachers' year plans in order to establish whether they are addressing curriculum expectations. Year plans are like road maps that show the major stopping points for the year ahead. They often look like calendars or charts and show how the various units will be scheduled during the year and the amount of time that will be spent on each unit. See Table 5.1 for an example of a year plan format.

An alternative format for a year plan allows room for a teacher to provide a rationale for why a unit is scheduled at a particular time of year. For example, a year plan may show that a teacher plans a *Rocks and Minerals* unit in September and October, that he wants to take advantage of anticipated good weather to take the children outside, and that approximately 7 weeks will be spent on the unit (see the partial year plan in Table 5.2).

Some practical issues need to be considered as you develop your year plan. One issue involves the availability of resources to help you teach your unit. In some schools, science and technology materials are in short supply and you may have to rely on kits that are circulated within your school district or province. If this

is the case, sometimes your decision about when to teach a unit will be dictated by the availability of the kits. Another issue to consider is the local weather. Units that benefit from outdoor experiences (e.g., studies of local ecosystems) should be scheduled during more moderate months. Other units (e.g., electricity) can be successfully conducted indoors. You should also consider the logical

Table 5.1
Sample One: Science Year Plan

Topic	Time of Year	Length of Time
(e.g., Rocks and Minerals)	(e.g., September)	(e.g., number of weeks)

Table 5.2
Sample Two: Science Year Plan

September	October
Topic: Rocks and Minerals	**Topic:** Rocks and Minerals
Rationale: Rocks and Minerals will be done in September and October to allow the students to go outside to explore different rocks and soils types in the local community. Students will also observe the types of vegetation association with different soil types and steps that have been taken to conserve soil	**Rationale:** Continued from September.
November **Topic:** **Rationale:**	**December** **Topic:** **Rationale:**
January **Topic:** **Rationale:**	**February** **Topic:** **Rationale:**

sequence of units within the school year. Sometimes a unit (e.g., exploring your senses) contains some basic concepts and skills that you can then build upon in subsequent units. The Senses unit, therefore, would be scheduled at the beginning of the school year. Another factor to think about is the potential integration with other subject areas. For example, you may plan a unit that includes studying an area plot on the school grounds at the same time that you are teaching a mathematics unit on measurement and estimation. Or, you may plan to teach a unit on building structures concurrently with a social studies unit on some ancient civilization renowned for their construction methods. A final consideration is the scheduling of other school activities and holidays. School concerts, holidays, and spring break mean that some months (e.g., December) have reduced time available, and you have to make some

Figure 5.1
Sample Conceptual Framework: Building With a Variety of Materials

1. **Structures and devices can be made with a variety of materials (e.g., plastic, paper, and wood).**

   1.1 The choice of materials depends on the need being met by the structure or device (e.g., wood for strength).

   1.2 Materials can be joined in a variety of different ways (e.g., with glue).

   1.3 Materials can be manipulated in a variety of ways (e.g., waxing paper increases its ability to be waterproof).

   1.4 Materials can be classified according to a variety of properties (e.g., classifying materials on the basis of strength).

   1.5 Materials can be evaluated.

2. **Tools must be matched with the appropriate material and use (e.g., saws are used to cut wood, scissors are used to cut paper).**

   2.1 Tools should be used in a safe manner (e.g., safety glasses should be worn).

3. **Structures and devices are designed to meet some need.**

   3.1 Structures and devices are constructed of purposeful components (e.g., model bridges have a variety of parts that fulfill different purposes).

4. **All technological solutions have trade-offs.**

   4.1 Structures and devices are designed within a field of constraints (e.g., cost constraints).

careful decisions about how to schedule units so that you can maintain continuity.

Unit Plans and Conceptual Frameworks

Each topic listed in your year plan should be developed into a unit plan. Usually a unit plan is created several weeks in advance of teaching the unit to allow time for you to consider important ideas about children's learning and teaching. These important ideas were mentioned in other chapters and include thinking about your understanding of the topic and your children, and considering what teaching resources, teaching, and assessment strategies to use.

We believe that another critical idea to consider prior to creating a unit plan concerns the conceptual goals for the unit. Questions such as "What are the concepts that should underpin activities? and How can concepts be linked together?" are important to answer before selecting activities and teaching strategies. One way in which teachers can map out unit concepts and the relationship among them is to construct a conceptual framework prior to creating the unit plan. A conceptual framework lists the general and specific concepts that will form the basis of the unit and helps teachers to think about why they are going to do particular activities. A sample conceptual framework is shown in Figure 5.1.

In the conceptual framework above, general and specific concepts have been listed for a unit on *Building With a Variety of Materials*. The conceptual framework provides the big picture of the unit and helps teachers think about important concepts related to unit activities. (Turn to the Companion Manual Part D for conceptual frameworks aligned with the Alberta program.)

Conceptual frameworks can be extended to include specific information from your local curriculum documents and can even be a useful place to jot down your first ideas about potential activities (see Figure 5.2).

Notice that Figure 5.2 features three Specific Learner Expectations that can be used to help students understand that structures and devices can be made with a variety of materials. From a constructivist perspective, this would allow the children to revisit this important concept within the context of at least three activities. Revisiting a concept within two or more lessons allows the time for students to construct a deeper and more meaningful understanding of the concept. (For ideas about the interrelationship between unit plans and conceptual frameworks, go to the Companion Manual and do Textbook Activity 5.3.)

Figure 5.2

Sample Conceptual Framework: Inserting Specific Learner Expectations

1. **Structures and devices can be made with a variety of materials (e.g., plastic, paper, and wood) (SLE 1, 2, 4).**

    1.1 The choice of materials depends on the need being met by the structure or device (e.g., wood for strength) (SLE 1, 2).

    1.2 Materials can be joined in a variety of different ways (e.g., with glue) (SLE 4).

    1.3 Materials can be manipulated in a variety of ways (e.g., waxing paper increases its ability to be waterproof) (SLE 1, 2).

    1.4 Materials can be classified according to a variety of properties (e.g., classifying materials on the basis of strength) (SLE 1).

    1.5 Materials can be evaluated (SLE 2).

Once you have constructed a conceptual framework for your unit and inserted specific information from your local curriculum documents, you should think about how to use the framework to create a unit plan. Unit plans can vary in format from a concise chart to more detailed account of all the objectives, materials, and strategies for each lesson. A sample unit plan chart that contains basic ideas to help teach a unit is shown in Table 5.3.

Teachers use their conceptual frameworks, program documents, and teaching resources to help create their unit plan charts. The first column (concepts) can easily be completed by retrieving this information from your conceptual framework. The second column (link to curriculum expectations) contains statements from local curriculum documents (in Alberta, these are the Specific Learner Expectations) that align with the concepts. Together, the first and second columns show your understanding of the important knowledge underpinning local curriculum expectations. Columns three, four, and five provide a brief description of the student activity that is linked to the concept and curriculum. In the last column, you can jot down how you intend to assess the students' understanding. Each completed line on the chart would then be developed into a detailed lesson plan.

Sometimes it is tempting to complete every line on the unit plan chart prior to beginning a unit. Teaching resources contain many fascinating activities and these activities can quickly fill the chart (See Appendix D for a list of excellent teaching resources and websites.). It is important, however, to leave room in your unit plans for your students. During some lessons, especially those at the beginning of the unit, you may spend time talking to the students about the unit and exploring the ideas and questions that they are bringing to the unit. On other days, you may want to spend time having the students work on investigations that are based on their personal questions. There will be other days on which you must pause and challenge some of the unhelpful ideas the students may have that stand to block them from understanding some concept. Unit plans, therefore, provide details of the overall story–line of the unit but some of the plot twists will only be revealed as you work with the students.

A challenging aspect of unit planning is to try and judge what would be a logical sequence of activities. Some

Table 5.3

Sample Unit Plan Chart

Concept(s)	Link to Curriculum Expectations	Brief Activity Description	Teaching Resource (e.g., title and page number)	Approximate Time	Assessment

teachers advise that you need to start with the students and their ideas and then build from this foundation. Other teachers may advise that you need to analyze the concepts, decide which concepts contain the most fundamental ideas that students will need to complete the unit, and begin with those concepts. Still other teachers may advise that you need to begin with discussing the nature of science and technology with your students and then continually revisit these ideas as you involve them in unit activities. All of these ideas for beginning and then sequencing the unit have merit and reflect different teaching philosophies. Probably what is most important to remember as you teach the unit, is that you should continually reflect on your plans so that you will develop a sense for how to begin and sequence the unit. Develop the habit of writing notes on each unit that you teach. Jot down what seemed to work, what the students still needed to understand in order to make productive connections between ideas, and how the unit could be taught better next time. Finally, know that you will never have a unit that represents the best way to teach all students. Different groups of students will have different ideas and needs and adapting a unit to meet those needs is part of the craft of teaching. (To think about how to sequence lessons, go to the Companion Manual and do Textbook Activity 5.4.)

Lesson Plans

Lesson plans are written for each lesson that you list in your unit plan. Sometimes a lesson can be concluded in 45-60 minutes, while other lessons may span several days. Lesson plans should contain enough detail to help you engage the students in the lesson, guide the children through the lesson, and know whether they have attained lesson objectives. Lesson plans should also have a length and format that is manageable and easy to access. A simple rule you can use to guide the length of your lesson plans is that each plan should be no more than one double–sided page.

A key question to ask as you begin to think about writing a lesson plan is: Why am I teaching this lesson? Are you hoping to help the students understand a difficult concept, or are you hoping to give them practice in conducting student–led investigations, or are you hoping to challenge some misconception that has arisen? Your answer to why you are teaching the lesson provides the frame on which you will attach various components of the lesson plan. Questions that can guide your thinking about components of a lesson plan include:

- *What do I want the students to learn?* Select the concepts, skills, and attitudes that you want to focus on during the lesson. Use Chapter 3 and Part D of the Companion Manual to help you think of the range of concepts, skills, and attitudes that could be included in a lesson. Think about the nature of science and technology the students will learn through participating in the lesson. Use Chapter 1 to help you think about how your perceptions of science and technology can influence your students' beliefs.

- *What will I do in order to facilitate that learning?* Think about different teaching strategies you have seen that can be used to explore students' ideas, link the lesson to their lives and to other lessons, engage them in thinking about the lesson, and guide them through obstacles. Use Chapter 4 to help you think about the range of teaching strategies you can select.

- *What will the students do in order to learn?* Think about the combination of physical and mental activity the students will need to do in order to learn. Use chapters 2 and 4 to help you consider the importance of including opportunities to share ideas, ask questions, write about ideas, draw pictures, and work with manipulatives.

- *How will I know if the students have understood the lesson?* Think about the evidence you will need to collect in order to conclude whether the students have understood the lesson. Use Chapter 6 to help you to consider what you should do before, during, and after the lesson in order to gather evidence on the students' thinking.

As you think about the questions listed above, you can begin to jot down ideas and organize these ideas into a lesson plan format. One common lesson plan format that can be used in any subject area is shown in Figure 5.3.

In the above lesson plan, teachers are given room to list the objectives of the lesson, the teaching resource used to help create the activity, lesson materials, and the instructional strategies to be used to teach and assess the lesson. Lesson objectives describe the student behaviors or performances that you would like them to work towards. Objectives in science, technology and STS lessons can list the concepts (the important ideas that underpin the lesson), skills (psychomotor, social, and problem-solving skills), and attitudes (ideas related to the values and habits of mind) that you want students to work towards during the lesson. The introduction, development, and closure describe the intended

Figure 5.3

Sample One: Lesson Plan

Topic:

Objectives (Concepts, Skills, and Attitudes):

Teaching Resource / Materials:

Introduction:

Development:

Closure:

Assessment:

sequence of the lesson and the way in which you will guide the students' actions and thinking. Cuing questions should be included in each of these three sections. These questions serve as springboards to assess existing ideas, the acquisition of new knowledge, and understanding of that knowledge. An alternative lesson plan format is shown in Figure 5.4.

In the lesson plan shown above, teachers use a different format to record information similar to that listed in Figure 5.3. Both sample lesson plans feature the critical areas of thought that all teachers should consider when planning effective lessons.

When you plan for scientific inquiry, generic lesson plans can be expanded to provide details about how to interact with the students to support their learning.

Figure 5.5 shows how ideas about how children learn, the nature of science, and what students should be learning combine to provide a context in which students can grow towards scientific literacy.

Figure 5.5 provides a template you can adapt to write scientific inquiry plans. With time, you will place emphasis on different aspects of the plan in order to reflect a variety of lesson intents and contexts.

Figure 5.6 shows how ideas about the nature of technological problem solving can be used to help differentiate a technology lesson from a science lesson.

Note that Figure 5.6 incorporates time to discuss the need that is met by the technological device or product, emphasizes the design process, and encourages the students to use pragmatic criteria to evaluate their product. These lesson features should be a part of all building activities you plan for your students and they should be made aware of how these lesson elements help to distinguish these activities from science.

Figure 5.4

Sample Two: Lesson Plan

Lesson Purpose:	Concepts:
	Skills:
	Attitudes:
Introduction: Development: Closure:	Time and Resources:
Assessment:	

Figure 5.7 shows how ideas related to STS decision–making can be incorporated into a lesson plan.

Note that Figure 5.7 incorporates ideas from the STS decision-making model discussed in chapters 3 and 4 and features a balanced, informed approach to decision-making and the flexibility for including several options for taking action.

After teaching each lesson, you should spend time reflecting on the successes and failures of the lesson. Ask yourself: What was the most successful aspect of the lesson? What would I do differently? How could I modify this lesson to expand learning? What additional resources would have enhanced this lesson? In what ways could the students have been more active participants in my lesson? (To understand how to reflect on a lesson, turn to your Companion Manual and do Textbook Activity 5.5.)

Figure 5.5
Scientific Inquiry Lesson Plan

Objectives
Concept(s):
What do you want the students to move towards understanding today?

e.g., Living things are affected by the nonliving features of their environment (e.g., climate, soil, light, and water availability).

Skill(s):
What skills will be a part of this lesson?

e.g., Mapping the living and nonliving features of a habitat.

Identifying links between living and nonliving things.

Communicating ideas about interrelationships.

Attitude(s):
What attitudes will be part of this lesson?

e.g., Perseverance in drawing a detailed map.

Respect for other students' opinions and viewpoints.

Introduction

• Discuss the questions, activity or content to be explored in this lesson.

• Review concepts/findings from previous lessons that are related to this lesson. Use a list of pre-planned questions to explore students' existing ideas.

• Establish a context for today's lesson (e.g., using visuals, a demonstration, storytelling, questions, etc.).

Development

• Review activity directions or brainstorm with students about how they will carry out the investigation.

• Encourage the students to make predictions about the outcome of the investigation or formulate a hypothesis that can be tested.

• Review safety precautions and time available for the activity.

• Discuss with the students how they might record information (e.g., using sentences, pictures, tables, graphs, lists, etc.).

• Model recording procedures for your students (e.g., model graphs, tables, charts, and anecdotal records).

• Provide guidance and ask questions during student activity. Have the students record additional questions that arise.

• Allow time to carry out the investigation and share ideas during the investigation.

• Encourage the students to seek patterns or regularities in the results and construct explanations and conclusions based on the evidence.

• Have the students write about the thoughts and reasons behind their interpretations and draw connections between cause and effect.

Closure

• Have the students present their findings (e.g., using graphs, charts, journal entries, drawings, models, etc.) and communicate how they conducted the investigation.

• Assist the students to clarify findings and questions, and identify problems.

• Discuss the merits of various solutions and findings and identify the variables that could have resulted in a variety of findings.

• Relate the findings to the activity purpose, previous lessons, and the students' initial ideas.

• Encourage the students to think about how what they learned today can be used to solve and explain everyday problems and events.

• Allot time in subsequent lessons for the students to explore their suggestions and questions.

Assessment

• How will you know if the students have begun to move towards an understanding of today's concepts, skills, and attitudes?

Figure 5.6

Technological Problem-Solving Lesson Plan

Objectives

Concept(s):

What do you want the students to move towards understanding today?

> e.g., Structures and devices can be made with a variety of materials (e.g., plastic, paper, and wood).

Skill(s):

What skills will be a part of this lesson?

> e.g., Drawing a picture of the intended structure.
>
> Selecting a variety of materials.
>
> Joining materials together.
>
> Evaluating the strength of the design.

Attitude(s):

What attitudes will be part of this lesson?

> e.g., Inventiveness in constructing a strength test.
>
> Perseverance in completing the structure.
>
> Willingness to base conclusions on their own experience.

Introduction

- Discuss the purpose of the activity or the need that is being met by the device or product to be designed and constructed.
- Discuss what values are reflected in the need for the product or device.
- Review findings from previous lesson(s) related to this lesson. Use a list of preplanned questions to probe the students' existing ideas.
- Establish a context for today's lesson (e.g., using visuals, brief demonstration, story-telling, questions, etc.).

Development

- Review activity directions and/or discuss with the students how they will carry out the activity.
- Discuss with the students how they might design and make the purposeful product.
- Encourage the students to prepare design proposals and present these proposals to other students.
- Guide the students to work collaboratively to construct the device or product.
- Review safety precautions and time available for the activity.
- Encourage the students to keep records of their ongoing evaluation of the evolving design.
- Assist the students to use pragmatic criteria (e.g., durability, cost-effectiveness, and reliability) to evaluate their devices and products.
- Allow students time to work together to carry out investigation, troubleshoot, and attempt a variety of strategies.

Closure

- Have the students present their findings (e.g., graphs, charts, journal entries, drawings, models, etc.).
- Discuss the challenges encountered while taking different approaches to designing and building.
- Have the students share written reports of design changes made and the reasons behind the design changes.
- Relate the findings to the activity purpose, previous lessons, and the students' initial ideas.
- Discuss how what was learned today could be used to design and build other products and devices.

Assessment

- How will you know if the students have begun to move towards understanding today's concepts, skills, and attitudes?

Figure 5.7
STS Decision-Making Lesson Plan

Objectives
Concept(s):
What do you want the students to move towards understanding today?
> e.g.,   Consumer products are the primary source of human waste.

Skill(s):
What skills will be a part of this lesson?
> e.g.,   Locating and organizing information about how cereal can be packaged.
>
> Identifying alternative ways to package cereal.
>
> Deciding on a course of action for purchasing cereal products and
>
> carrying out that action.

Attitude(s):
What attitudes will be part of this lesson?
> e.g.,   Respect for the rights and opinions of others.
>
> Responsibility towards the environment.

Introduction
- Discuss the issue to be explored in this lesson.
- Review the science and technology from previous lessons that are related to this issue.
- Use a list of pre-planned questions to explore students' existing ideas.
- Establish a context for the issue (e.g., using visuals, a demonstration, storytelling, questions, etc.).

Development
- Assist children to locate and organize information related to the issue (e.g., using the Internet, print resources, questionnaires, surveys, etc.).
- Identify different alternatives related to the issue.
- Model how the students will track alternatives and varying viewpoints (e.g., charts, graphs, and anecdotal records).
- Provide guidance and ask questions (e.g., What are the reasons behind various alternatives and viewpoints? and What values do these viewpoints reflect?)
- Compare and contrast different points of view.
- Assist children to gain a balanced view of the issue.
- Decide on a course of action and predict the consequences of different courses of action.
- Take personal or group action (e.g., change in consumer preferences or a change in purchasing choices).

Closure
- Have the students communicate their decision-making and the consequences of their actions (e.g., written and verbal reports).
- Assist the children to clarify their reasoning and identify the challenges inherent in taking action.
- Discuss the merits of different courses of action.
- Evaluate the decision-making process.
- Relate the lesson to the activity purpose and to previous lessons.
- Discuss the potential longevity of different courses of action.

Assessment
- How will you know if the students have begun to move towards an understanding of today's concepts, skills, and attitudes?

Daily Plan Books

A final level of planning useful for teachers is a daily plan book. These books are usually coil–bound and can be purchased at office supply stores. Each page of the book is a separate day where you can jot down a very brief summary of your teaching in addition to assorted notes and reminders. Figure 5.8 shows a typical page from a daily plan book.

Figure 5.8
Sample Daily Plan Book

Date:	Reminders:
Morning: • • • • Afternoon: • • • •	Notes:

Daily plan books provide an overall picture of the school year and are useful for showing the actual pace of your units and lessons versus the planned pace found in your year and unit plans. Information can be compared to your year and unit plans and necessary adjustments for the following year can be made. Daily plan books also provide an easily accessible format that can be used to quickly answer inquiries from a parent whose child has been absent on a particular day.

Summary Ideas

This chapter presents some current thinking about:

- *Why planning is important.* Planning is a critical component of effective teaching. Written plans allow teachers to create a pedagogical record of original plans, revisions to those plans, and reflections on how to change the plans for next year.

- *What guidelines teachers follow when preparing to teach.* Teachers consider the content of the local curriculum, their background knowledge of the topic, the characteristics of their students, the availability of teaching resources, the types of teaching strategies that can be used, and how they will assess their students' learning.

- *How to write long–range and short–range plans.* Teachers need to develop year plans, unit plans, conceptual frameworks, and lesson plans. Daily plan books are a useful addition to these plans. Several formats can be used for each of these levels of planning and teachers should eventually develop an approach to planning that reflects their philosophy of teaching.

- *How scientific inquiry, technological problem solving, and STS decision-making plans differ.* All kinds of plans emphasize the development of concepts, skills, and attitudes. Scientific inquiry plans emphasize inquiring into a scientific question, formulating an explanation, and evaluating that explanation in light of alternatives. Technological problem-solving plans, however, emphasize the need being met by the device or product, the skills involved in designing the device or product, and the need to use pragmatic criteria (e.g., durability and cost-effectiveness) to evaluate the device or product. STS decision-making plans emphasize gathering and interpreting information, investigating a number of perspectives, deciding on a course of action, taking action, and evaluating that action.

Making Productive Connections
Scenario 1

You have just been hired to teach Grade 6. Your school district's science program lists five topics for Grade 6–*Air and Aerodynamics, Flight, Sky Science, Evidence and Investigations,* and *Trees and Forests.* Construct a year plan for these topics that outlines the sequence in which you would teach the topics and the rationale for why you selected that sequence.

Scenario 2

The children in your kindergarten science class wonder where butterflies come from. Construct a conceptual framework for a unit on butterflies that will help them answer this and other related questions.

Scenario 3

The children in your Grade 6 classroom are very interested in playing computer games in their leisure time. How would you plan to include this interest in your science program?

Scenario 4

The children in your Grade 1 science class notice that many dandelions are blooming in the schoolyard. How would you plan to use the students' interest in dandelions in your school science program?

Ideas to Think About When Teaching Science, Technology, and Society

- How do I plan lessons to help students understand connections between concepts?

- How do I use a conceptual framework to focus my thoughts about a unit?

- How do I include my students' existing ideas in my daily teaching strategies?

- How do I record my reflections on the success of the lesson so that I can access this information next year?

- How do I help every student make a personal connection to the lesson?

Selected Readings

Burden, P.R. & Byrd, D.M. (1998). *Methods for Effective Teaching (2nd edition)*. Boston, MA: Allyn and Bacon.

The authors present some of the fundamental principles of effective teaching such as: preparing for instruction, organizing and managing instruction, considering learners' needs, and assessing student performance.

Harlen, W. (2000). *The Teaching of Science in Primary Schools (3rd edition)*. London: David Fulton Publishers.

This well-known British author provides information about a variety of topics related to teaching elementary science such as: how teachers can help children construct ideas, the meaning of progression in learning science, the role of language and discussion, how to cope with children's science questions, and the value of helping children to reflect on their approach to problem solving.

Hausfather, S.J. (1992). It's time for a conceptual change. *Science and Children, 30*(3), 22-23.

The author presents some practical suggestions for using a conceptual change approach to teaching. He emphasizes the need to have flexible plans that allow

teachers to find out what their students know, and then design classroom activities that help students learn with understanding.

Selected Websites

SAMPLE SCIENCE LESSON PLANS
http://www.col-ed.org/cur/science.html#sci1
This website contains a wide variety of science lesson plans that have been submitted by practicing teachers.

ASKERIC LESSON PLANS
http://askeric.org/Virtual/Lessons/
This website features lesson plans categorized by subject. Science lesson plans span all concept areas and are suitable for a variety of grades.

TEACHNET.COM
http://www.teachnet.com/lesson.html
This website features lessons from all subject areas including science. Lessons range from earth, life, and physical sciences to technology topics.

DESIGN TECHNOLOGY TEACHING IDEAS
http://www.teachingideas.co.uk/dt/contents.htm
This website provides some design technology lesson plans and activity ideas for all ages.

ACTIVITIES INTEGRATING MATH AND SCIENCE (AIMS)
http://www.aimsedu.org/
This website features a great teaching resource consisting of classroom activities on a variety of science topics.

GREAT EXPLORATIONS IN MATH AND SCIENCE (GEMS)
http://www.lhs.berkeley.edu/GEMS/
This website features an exceptional teaching resource consisting of classroom activities on a variety of science topics.

FULL OPTION SCIENCE SYSTEM (FOSS)
http://lhsfoss.org/
This website features a great teaching resource consisting of classroom activities on a variety of science topics.

Chapter 6
Assessing Children's Learning in STS

Learning Objectives

In this chapter, you should learn

- What assessment is.
- Strategies for assessing students before, during, and after learning.
- How to assess concepts, skills, and attitudes.
- How students and teachers can self-assess.

Thinking About Your Existing Ideas

Write down your answers to the following questions. After you complete this chapter, revisit your answers. Which of your ideas remained the same and which changed? How did they change, and what do you believe caused the changes?

- What does the term "assessment" mean to you?
- Why do teachers assess students' learning?
- What does a teacher need to know and be able to do to assess learning?
- How should learning be assessed?
- How can assessment be fair and authentic?
- How do you think your beliefs about assessment methods will influence your approach to teaching scientific inquiry, technological problem-solving, and STS decision-making?

To understand assessment and the many roles it plays in science and technology education, you first need to look at the 'big picture' by thinking about how the socio-cultural context influences what various interest groups (stakeholders) believe assessment is and what its purposes are. For example, politicians may believe that implementing standardized achievement tests demonstrates accountability to the electorate. Parents may endorse particular kinds of assessment such as multiple choice tests because these are familiar, traditional approaches. School districts may use assessment to judge the effectiveness of teachers, programs, and school districts. Teachers may use assessment to probe students' understanding and report progress to parents.

As a teacher, you need to become an informed consumer of educational trends, especially those that surround the often contentious issue of assessment. For example, when you hear that assessment might be used to investigate whether teachers are being accountable, you should ask, "Whose interests are served by this trend? What does it mean for teachers to be accountable? Who are they accountable to? How does this enhance children's learning? What should teachers do?"

What is most important for you to keep in mind as you think about the issues surrounding assessment is that your assessments are not ends in themselves but, like all your other classroom activities, aim at enhancing student learning. You gather assessment information primarily to inform and improve your future teaching.

Experience demonstrates that this is best done when you become familiar with and use a variety of assessment strategies. There is no one best strategy; every strategy has its advantages and disadvantages. By using different strategies you retain the advantages of a specific strategy while addressing its disadvantages through using other strategies. Finally, as is often the case in teaching, balance is a useful guideline. Your assessment needs to be as fair and authentic as you can make it but at the same time it must take into account the practicalities of your classroom. (Go to your Companion Manual, Textbook Activity 6.1 and think about the purposes of assessment in light of your own assessment experiences as a student.)

What is Assessment?

"What did you get?" Every teacher has heard this question asked by one student to another in reference to the results of assessment. The question "What did you learn?" is seldom heard in similar circumstances. The juxtaposition of these two queries demonstrates how much current assessment is seen by students and others to focus on grades rather than on learning, even though grading is just a small part of what assessment is all about.

What is assessment? Assessment is an information-gathering process that encompasses all activities in which students are asked to demonstrate what they know, understand, and can do. Teachers gather this information using a variety of assessment strategies that allow them to observe students and gather samples of their thinking about scientific and technological activities. Teachers interpret this information and use these judgments to:

- Provide students with information about their progress, strengths, and areas for improvement.
- Report students' progress to other groups (e.g., parents).
- Modify instructional strategies to better help students learn.
- Make decisions about what to teach in the future.
- Determine student placement in programs that can provide the support they need.

Learning and assessment are closely linked and there are a variety of conditions needed for students to learn and do well on assessments. These conditions include:

- *Teacher's pedagogical content knowledge.* Teachers with well-developed knowledge of subject matter, pedagogy, learners, classrooms, and curricula are better able to plan activities and experiences for students that will enhance their understanding and improve their ability to succeed in assessment tasks.
- *Coordination of teaching with assessment strategies.* For students to do well on assessment, the teacher must ensure that the content and teaching strategies used to help the students learn the concepts, skills, and attitudes are well coordinated with the assessment strategies.

- *Time available for teaching and learning.* The constructivist view of learning emphasizes that it takes time for students to identify their existing ideas, consider new ideas presented in class, and work towards restructuring the old with the new. Students need to revisit the same concept within a number of contexts to construct a meaningful understanding.

- *Availability of quality teaching resources.* Quality teaching resources should recommend teaching strategies and materials to help students learn what is important, and should provide also ideas about assessing that learning fairly and authentically

Assessment Language

You need to be familiar with terms that describe common assessment principles. One group of terms helps describe the purpose and timing of various assessment strategies:

- *Formative assessment (Continuous assessment).* Monitors students' ongoing progress to help students learn and to help teachers reflect on and modify their instructional strategies.

- *Summative assessment.* Provides a summary of each student's learning, usually in the form of a unit-ending test, that shows how students' thinking has changed and the nature of their final understandings.

- *Diagnostic assessment.* Gathers comprehensive, in-depth information about a specific area of understanding to find out what students know and can do.

A second group of common assessment terms focuses on the kinds of standards against which students' work can be judged.

- *Criterion referenced.* Judging a student's work against an established standard for acceptable performance (e.g., knowing certain ideas).

- *Norm referenced.* Judging a student's work against a larger representative reference group (e.g., all students in the province).

- *Self referenced.* Judging the student against his or her own progress (e.g., comparing a pre–test to a post–test).

A pair of terms focuses on the dependability of the assessment strategies, which is achieved through balancing validity and reliability.

- *Validity* refers to how well the assessment strategy measures what it was intended to measure.

- *Reliability* refers to the degree to which you would obtain a similar result if the assessment strategy were repeated.

An assessment strategy that when repeated results in very similar student scores has a high degree of reliability. However, achieving this sometimes requires narrowing both the questions (e.g., to measuring discrete bits of knowledge), and the strategy (e.g., to solely multiple choice items) to the point that validity may be compromised. Conversely, an assessment strategy that is more valid (e.g., asking students to write their own explanations for a scientific phenomenon) may be less reliable as it demands a greater degree of teacher judgment. You need to choose an assessment strategy that both fulfils the intended purpose and strikes a reasonable balance between validity and reliability.

A final pair of terms focuses on the source of the assessment.

- *Internal* assessments are set by the teacher and usually involve asking children to think in a variety of ways about the concepts, skills, and attitudes they were taught.

- *External* assessments are set by people or organizations, e.g., government-appointed committees, that are situated outside the classroom.

Although certain interest groups claim that external assessments help hold teachers accountable, it is difficult to design external assessments that genuinely evaluate students' understanding, skill, and attitude development. Many external assessments feature a multiple choice format which makes it hard to validly measure higher level thinking skills (e.g., thinking critically or evaluating data) and group attitudes (e.g., cooperating with others and respecting other students' ideas). Further, high stakes multiple choice tests can lead to both teaching for the test and memorization without understanding. Although featuring a high degree of reliability, then, external assessments are criticized for their low validity.

Fair and Authentic Assessment

In the past, *fair assessment* meant assessment was based on what was taught, measured what it was supposed to measure, and resulted in a good distribution of grades. Recently, the notion of fair assessment has been expanded to include the following:

- Accessible to the range of students in today's inclusive classrooms, including those with learning disabilities, physical disabilities, and limited English proficiency. Modifications may include re-thinking how questions are presented and communicating using a number of different modes (e.g., verbal, written or pictorial).

- Free from gender and racial bias.

- Sensitive to the contexts in which students live (e.g., designed using questions that are set within common life and community-based experiences).

Authentic assessment refers to assessment that is more practical, realistic, and challenging. Identified characteristics of authentic assessment include:

- *Aligned with the curriculum and with instruction.* Curriculum alignment helps teachers know whether they are testing what they teach. Instructional alignment involves matching instructional strategies to assessment strategies (e.g., using hands-on assessment to evaluate hands–on instruction).

- *Asks students to engage in more complex tasks.* More complex tasks could include extended scientific investigations, designing and making a product to fulfill a need, or reviewing Internet web sites to write a research report on an important STS issue.

- *Includes student self–assessment.* Students are provided with assessment expectations (e.g., a rubric containing detailed criteria), and are made responsible for monitoring their own assessment and learning.

- *Requires students to apply knowledge, skills, and attitudes to situations outside the classroom.* Students are challenged by questions and problems similar to those experienced by scientists and technologists.

Authentic assessment poses a number of challenges for teachers.

- *Manageability.* Authentic assessments can take up a large amount of classroom time.

- *Familiarity.* Students may be unfamiliar with the kinds of open–ended, higher level questions that are required.

- *Inclusiveness.* Some students may have difficulty reading and understanding the more demanding language required to frame questions for authentic assessments.

- *Reliability.* The increased validity of authentic assessment may result in less reliability.

- *Generalizability.* Authentic assessments tend to be geared towards a limited sample of concepts, skills, and attitudes so it is difficult to generalize results to an entire unit.

To overcome these challenges, you need to understand that balance is the key to successful authentic assessment. Through balancing authentic assessment with more traditional forms of assessment (e.g., multiple choice), you can still gather useful information to guide decisions about future teaching and to evaluate student progress.

(Go to your Companion Manual, Textbook Activity 6.2 and consider the fairness and authenticity of some items on a standardized achievement test.)

Thinking About Assessment

Although you will be assessing concepts, skills, and attitudes using a variety of assessment strategies, you can be guided in your efforts by an overall pattern of thinking.

- *Think about the purpose of gathering the assessment information.* Sometimes you may have just one purpose in mind (e.g., finding out what students know about a discrete concept or calculating a grade). On other occasions you may want the assessment to serve several purposes (e.g., reveal students' strengths and weaknesses and serve as a guide for modifying teaching strategies).

- *Design assessment strategies to gather the required information.* You need to select an appropriate strategy by considering factors such as the purpose of your assessment, whether you will have students participate in assessment before, during, or after the lesson, and what selection of concepts, skills, and attitudes you will address. You need to balance validity and reliability, as well as apply principles of fair and authentic assessment to ensure all students can understand and relate to the assessment.

- *Make judgments about the students' work.* You will often have to develop the criteria against which you make your judgments. Keep in mind that there are different ways to judge students' work—norm-referenced, criterion-referenced, and self-referenced.

- *Use assessment results to make decisions about future teaching and learning.* You need to consider the actions you might take based on your assessment data. Will you re–teach a lesson or devise an alternative teaching strategy that can better help the students? Will some students need additional support? Will other students' benefit from additional enrichment activities and more independent work?

Despite teachers' best efforts to design and implement good classroom assessment, questions remain about what can be accomplished by assessment and to what extent assessment negatively affects teaching and learning. Common criticisms are:

- Only trivial and easily measurable outcomes get assessed.

- Marks and grades have become ends unto themselves with students admitting that they memorize without understanding and teachers saying that they teach for the test.

- All assessment strategies are subject to interpretation and no approach seems completely fair.

Even methods of judging work that involve comparing to some referent are subject to criticism as the method used to describe and categorize the referent inevitably reflects the perspective of the developer. You can see that assessment is contentious and will long continue to be the subject of conversation among school stakeholders.

Assessment Feedback: When and What?

Assessment is a feedback process that provides information to the teacher about the effects of teaching. Feedback needs to be gathered at three main times:

- Before teaching to elicit the students' existing ideas.

- During teaching to find out what students are making of the teaching (formative evaluation).

- After teaching to find out if and how students' ideas have changed (summative evaluation).

Assessment feedback to teachers from students usually takes one of four forms:

- Verbal (e.g., responses to classroom questions during teaching).

- Written (e.g., paper and pencil tests, written journals).

- Visual (e.g., diagrams and drawings).

- Performance-based (e.g., completion of a hands-on task such as an experiment or building task).

Assessment Before Teaching

Why Assess Before Teaching?

Constructivist approaches to learning emphasize the need to find out students' ideas prior to teaching. Existing ideas provide:

- Baseline information about what students already know.

- Useful guidelines for how to plan and teach by

  - Uncovering students' alternative conceptions about the natural and manufactured world, which often differ from commonly accepted conceptions.

  - Indicating potential barriers to concepts you want to teach.

  - Showing gaps in the students' knowledge.

  - Suggesting how to connect what is to be taught with what children already know.

Strategies for assessing children's existing ideas include interviews, surveys, predictions and plans, and pre-tests and post-tests (see Chapter 2 for additional discussion about children's existing ideas).

Interviews About Events and Concepts

Interviewing children can help you uncover students' existing ideas. This strategy originated with Jean Piaget and was later taken up by constructivist educators. Interviews may be about a topic in general or can explore specific aspects of the topic. Two general interview approaches can be used:

- A controlled but flexible conversational interview usually accompanied by visual prompts such as diagrams, pictures, or objects.

- An interview centered around a task devised by the interviewer, e.g., testing the poles of magnets against each other to see how they attract or repel.

During interviews you need to know when to ask a question and what kind of question to ask. Always keep in mind that you are interviewing and not teaching. Your goal is not to judge the 'rightness' of the student's responses but to gather information, to get the student's ideas into your head rather than to get your ideas into the student's head. You must allow the student to take the lead in the interview, to talk freely, and to express ideas in her or his own words. Monitor your own performance during the interview and audiotape the interview so you have a record of what was said. Since individually interviewing twenty-five children is difficult in the classroom, instead you can ask each of your interview questions to all your students at the same time and ask them to respond in written form.

Here are some examples of some stems you can use to develop a list of interview questions:

- What do you notice about…?
- Can you explain to me why…?
- What happens when…?
- How would you describe…?
- Could you tell me what you just said in a different way?

Surveys of Children's Existing Ideas

Children's existing ideas can also be elicited by a written survey patterned after a multiple choice test. This is another practical way to find out the ideas of an entire class of children at the same time. To develop such surveys you need to know both the concepts that you are trying to teach and the children's typical alternative conceptions with respect to those concepts. Each survey item should:

- Focus on an important concept you are planning to teach.
- Be accompanied by a visual prompt (e.g., diagram, drawing).
- Include the scientific conception as one possible response.
- Base other possible responses on typical children's alternative conceptions.

It will take you several attempts and applications before you arrive at a satisfactory survey that will aid your teaching. Figure 6.1 provides a sample survey question that probes students' existing ideas about how light is refracted (bent).

Figure 6.1.

Sample Survey Question: The Reappearing Coin

A coin is placed in the middle of the bottom of a small plastic tub and stuck down with a piece of plasticine. Students move back from the tub until they just cannot see the coin, i.e., the coin is hidden by the side of the tub. While students stand in place, water is poured into the tub until each person slowly starts to see the coin again. The reason the coin is now visible is

(a) Water allows light to be reflected off the coin.

(b) Water magnifies the coin and makes it look bigger.

(c) The coin became unstuck and moved from the center of the tub.

(d) Water changes the direction of the light reflected off the coin.

Notice that in Figure 6.1 the students are provided with a short scenario (which would be accompanied by a diagram) followed by the possible responses they can choose from.

Predictions and Plans

Predictions–in the context of science–and plans–in the context of technology–also provide feedback for assessing children's existing ideas. Prediction is a scientific inquiry skill that uses existing data to propose inferences and patterns to suggest future outcomes. Children's predictions can be used to assess understanding because the accuracy of a prediction is based on the ability to gather and comprehend previous information. Inferences about student understanding can be drawn from both the prediction itself and the accompanying reasoning.

Plans are similar to predictions and are an important and authentic aspect of technological problem-solving. Plans require thinking ahead and, just like architects, engineers, and industrial designers, students need to work out in advance how they are going to solve a technological problem. Planning may occur at the start of a project (initial planning) and continue once the implementation of the design solution has begun (opportunistic planning). Planning usually includes visual representations such as diagrams and drawings, writing, and discussions with peers and the teacher. Plans can reveal how children:

- *Understand their resources, both material and time.* For example, a plan for a straw tower that indicates how many straws will be used.

- *Understand the various issues related to the project.* For example, a drawing that shows the details of how wheels and axles will be attached to a model car chassis.

- *Conceptualize the path to their solution.* For example, a drawing that identifies what parts of a boat will be changed to make it float better.

- *Visualize what the solution will look like.* For example, a diagram of the circuit for an electric buzzer.

Pre-Tests and Post-Tests

A powerful assessment strategy is pre-testing students to find out what they already know and then post-testing them after teaching to see what specific changes in understanding have occurred. Traditional paper and pencil tests can be used for this purpose but other types of assessments are also appropriate (e.g., written surveys). You must administer similar (but not identical) kinds of assessments for the pre-test and post-test to produce comparable results. For example, for both your pre-test and post-test you could use an activity where children test various household products with an indicator to find out whether they are acids or bases but you would vary the household products in both tests.

Some guidelines for developing pre-tests and post-tests are:

- Decide what you want students to learn (e.g., some knowledge such as the laws of magnetism, a skill such as hypothesizing, or an attitude such as open-mindedness).

- Decide how students will demonstrate the outcomes you want to assess (e.g., do an experiment, build a model, decide an issue).

- Ensure that the two assessments are similar in form and structure.

- Ensure that your pre-test is not graded but only provides a baseline for grading the post-test by revealing what students knew before you taught them.

Assessment During Teaching

Why Assess During Teaching?

Formative evaluation is carried out during teaching and involves monitoring student understanding while students are actively engaged in learning. You can think of formative assessment as an ongoing inquiry into what and how students are learning. The findings can help teachers document individual progress over time, convey expectations to students, and make judgments and decisions about learning both during the teaching and after the teaching is done. For example, during scientific inquiry, teachers engaging in formative assessment feedback can help students expand their thinking, steer their investigations in a more fruitful direction, and suggest alternative ways of looking at what is happening and why it is happening. Strategies for assessing students during teaching include rubrics, observation checklists and rating scales, anecdotal records, questioning, daily classroom talk, and daily written work records.

Using Rubrics

Rubrics are useful for evaluating a variety of kinds of student work. A rubric is typically a set of three to five key criteria used for assessing a comprehensive piece of work such as an inquiry into the role of switches in a circuit or the design of a model glider. Each criterion could have four quality gradations or levels, from one to four (e.g., poor, fair, good, or excellent; limited, adequate, proficient, or excellent). Level 3 is considered 'competence'. The levels include explanations as to how to identify each gradation of each criterion. Table 6.1 shows a typical generic rubric framework.

Table 6.1

Rubric Framework

	Level 1	Level 2	Level 3 (Competence)	Level 4
Criterion 1	(Identifying Level 1 of Criterion 1)	Etc.		
Criterion 2	Etc.			

Some advantages to using well-designed rubrics are that they:

- Make teacher expectations clear.
- Are easy to apply to student work.
- Reduce time spent assessing.
- Are easy to explain to students and parents.
- Are useful for both self and peer assessment.

Rubrics also have three main disadvantages:

- Good ones can be hard to create.
- They may be too specific and over-restrict the allowable responses.
- They may be too general and hence require too much teacher interpretation.

When designing rubrics you need to:

- *Use clear language.* For example, "Can explain that both bulbs remain lit when one switch is left open because each bulb has its own path to the battery" is better than "Knows how switches work."
- *Use criteria that distinguish clearly among levels.* For example, it is hard to differentiate between a "clear and detailed explanation" and a "logical explanation."
- *Balance the descriptions of the criteria between too general and too specific.* For example, "Uses previous knowledge in new situations" is very general while "Uses knowledge of stability to create a wide base" is more specific.

Each time you use your rubrics to evaluate student work, reflect on how well the criteria fulfilled your assessment needs and then improve them as required.

Tables 6.2, 6.3, and 6.4 provide some examples of rubric criteria.

Table 6.2: Rubric
Criteria for Knowledge of Rust

Rust Learning Expectations	Level 1	Level 2	Level 3 (Competency)	Level 4
Is a process of chemical change.	Is a process of change.	Is a process of physical change.	Is a process of chemical change.	Is a process of irreversible chemical change.
Requires iron, water, and oxygen.	Requires iron or water or oxygen.	Requires iron and water.	Requires iron, water, and oxygen.	Requires iron, water, and oxygen; water helps dissolve the iron.
Is a new substance.	Is the same as the metal.	Is partly the metal and partly a new substance.	Is a new substance.	Is a new substance and cannot be changed back into the metal.
Forms at the surface of the metal.	Is the same as the metal.	Forms inside the metal.	Forms at the surface of the metal.	Forms at the surface of the metal and can be prevented by coating the metal.

Table 6.3
Generic Rubric Criteria for the Skill of Predicting

	Level 1	Level 2	Level 3	Level 4
Predicting	Begins activity without making a prediction.	Prediction is made but no reason is given.	Prediction is made and a reason is given.	Prediction is made, a reason is given, and prediction is reconciled with actual result.

Table 6.4

Rubric Criteria To Assess the Stability of an Art Straw Tower

Level 1	Level 2	Level 3 (Competency)	Level 4
Tower cannot stand on its own.	Tower stands on its own but is unsteady.	Tower stands on its own and is steady.	Tower stands on its own, is steady, and remains steady. when blown upon by a fan set on low speed.

Observation Checklists and Rating Scales

As the children are working, you need to move about the room to observe what they are doing. You can use checklists and rating scales to keep track of your observations by recording whether and to what extent children exhibit behaviors which indicate the learning of desired concepts, skills, and attitudes. A checklist allows a teacher to record whether or not the behavior was observed. A rating scale indicates whether the behavior was observed as well as the degree to which it was observed. The main disadvantage of checklists and rating scales is the difficulty of finding time to do comprehensive and multiple observations of each child. A reasonable compromise would be to use just a few checklists and rating scales during each unit plan. Below is an example of a checklist (which could be converted into a rating scale by substituting numbers from 1–4 for the checks).

Anecdotal Records

Anecdotal records in the form of written teacher notes are less structured records of observations of individual students made while they work. The observations relate to an identified general purpose (e.g., use of evidence or collaboration during group work). The notes describe student-related incidents (e.g., a brief verbal exchange between two pupils), that the teacher judges are relevant to the general purpose of the observations. The notes also include the teacher's interpretation of what the incident reveals about the behaviors or attitudes of the students involved. The open-endedness of anecdotal records makes them richer in detail and more individualized than checklists and rating scales, and they can help build a comprehensive profile of a particular student. However, making systematic anecdotal records can be unwieldy and time consuming and they generally work better when used with smaller classes for simple purposes.

Table 6.5

Checklist for Utilizing Evidence

Utilizing Evidence	Alan	Beth	Curt	Dana	Evan	Faye
Places importance on the collection and use of evidence.						
Gathers evidence from a variety of sources.						
Gathers evidence with care.						
Distinguishes between relevant and irrelevant evidence.						
Makes evidence public and accessible.						
Bases reasoning about phenomena on evidence.						
Resolves discrepancies and disagreements in reasoning by referring back to evidence.						
Waits until available evidence is in before drawing conclusions.						
Shows willingness to change ideas, based on evidence.						

Questioning

While you are interacting with students you can use questioning to explore their ideas and thus obtain feedback about their thinking. Useful types of questions encourage students to think critically, explain their investigations, reflect on their experiences, apply their ideas to a range of applications, and consider alternatives. Examples of such questions include

- What are you doing?
- Why are you doing it?
- How are you doing it?
- What have you done so far?
- What else do you need to do?
- How could you approach this problem in another way?
- How else could you test this idea?
- What would happen if…?
- What were you trying to find out?
- Why did you do this?
- What problems have you encountered?
- How have you overcome your problems?
- How might you solve this problem?
- What other alternatives would you suggest?
- What do you predict would happen if…?
- What have your results to do with the problem you were trying to solve?
- How has your understanding changed as a result of your work?
- What did you find hard to do?
- Have you thought of …?
- How could you use these ideas to explain …?
- Another group came up with this solution … What do you think?

You should also note what questions your students ask you because they can indicate how they are reconstructing their ideas to make sense of the activity as well as the depth of their current understanding. You can actively encourage their queries by asking them to propose questions concerning what still puzzles them about particular aspects of their work. Student questions can indicate if you need to spend more time on the learning outcomes and can also be the starting points for new investigations.

Daily Classroom Talk

Classroom lessons involve numerous verbal exchanges between students and teacher and among students. Students and teachers ask and respond to questions, offer suggestions, present their views, elaborate on or respond to the views of others, choose between alternatives, make judgments, share ideas, and summarize learning. Daily classroom talk is a potentially rich source of assessment and alert teachers constantly monitor student talk to evaluate what they are making of the teaching. But classroom talk can be difficult to assess formally because it occurs while the teacher is fully engaged in teaching and it leaves no tangible records or artifacts for later review.

The best opportunities for assessing student talk are created when you formally bring all students together to discuss a specific lesson topic or activity. You must have an underlying purpose for these discussions and facilitate the dialogue so students exercise some control over the direction and substance of their comments. You should set the stage for the discussion but avoid dominating it, allowing students opportunities to develop ideas, to follow aspects of the topic that interest them, and to communicate their ideas in their own words. A flexible approach reveals thinking that may not become evident if students have to adhere more closely to the teacher's agenda.

Some guidelines to keep in mind when organizing such discussions:

- Start the discussion with open-ended questions that allow for a variety of responses. For example, "How might we make the parachute descend more slowly?"
- As the discussion continues, allow the children to shape its scope.
- Ensure all students participate and present their ideas.
- Audiotape the discussion or make notes, charts, or lists that capture the key aspects of the children's thinking.

Journals

Written work in a variety of forms is an important aspect of classroom lessons. You can provide students with journals in which they keep all their writing. The value and quality of written work depends both on how topics are taught and on the student's overall writing experience, including the value placed on writing. Daily written work is part of authentic science and technology, and helps students convey their thoughts and articulate their understandings, especially students who do not say much in class. Journals can include any or all of lists, observations, drawings and diagrams, tables and graphs, reflective thoughts, questions and responses, experimental write-ups, explanations, ideas for future investigation, and narrative descriptions.

Journals are useful for both formative and summative assessment. Analyzing the various items on a short-term basis provides insight into what students have accomplished at one particular point. Assessing a journal in its entirety (e.g., at the end of a unit), provides rich feedback on how students' knowledge, skills, and attitudes have changed over time. Assessing students' journal writing can include:

- Gaining an overall impression of the student's work (e.g., is it comprehensive, interesting, thoughtful, unusual, accurate?).

- Attending to specific details of writing and drawing and the understandings they reveal.

- Comparing earlier and later entries to evaluate progress.

- Holding a class or individual discussion after a particular phase of writing is completed so students can talk about what they have written and why.

You should provide written feedback to students about their writing by commenting on what is good and suggesting what could be reconsidered and elaborated on. Some useful structures for encouraging students to go further are:

- I wonder . . .?

- How could you use these ideas to explain . . .?

- What happens if . . .?

- What other explanations could there be?

- How else could you test this idea?

- How could you find out more?

(Go to your Companion Manual Textbook Activity 6.3 to think about some of the practical problems associated with formative assessment in the classroom.)

Assessment After Teaching

Why Assess After Teaching?

Summative assessment after teaching provides a summary of the achievements of individual children at particular times. It generally takes place when achievement or what has been learned needs to be reported to parents, administrators, and to the students themselves. Summative assessment may occur at regular intervals, as in a regular weekly test, or more commonly at the end of each unit of work or reporting term. Strategies for assessing children after teaching include conferencing, predict-observe-explain (POE), concept maps, drawings and diagrams, portfolios, products of practical work, performance-based tasks, and paper and pencil tests.

Conferencing

You can meet and talk with individual children or small groups of students both during and at the end of a unit. These meetings help build rapport and give you the opportunity to review work and question the children. You can also meet with individual students prior to sending home formal reports on their progress. Although conferencing should happen in all classrooms, it is particularly useful when teaching young students who lack the written skills necessary to express all of their ideas. Be sure to keep a record of the conference in the form of notes or even audiotapes.

POE (Predict-Observe-Explain)

A POE is a loose framework for carrying out scientific inquiry that can also be used for probing students' understanding. A POE can provide insight into how pupils understand situations and concepts, how they reason, and how and why their beliefs change. The procedure for a POE is as follows (White and Gunstone, 1992):

- Assist students in understanding the situation they will make a prediction about.

- Allow students to ask clarifying questions about the situation.

- Have students write down a prediction as to what will happen and their reasons for it, For example, "How will raisins behave when placed in water and fresh pop, respectively?"

- Have students write down their observations of what happens. For example, "Raisins in water sink to the bottom and stay there. Raisins in pop repeatedly gather bubbles, rise to the top, lose their bubbles, flip over, and sink to the bottom again."

- Have students explain differences between their predictions and their observations. For example, "Pop contains dissolved carbon dioxide gas while water does not."

- Have students carry out additional POEs by changing a significant variable. For example, use peanuts, grapes, carbonated water, stale pop, diet pop, etc.

You can assess pupil understanding by considering their beliefs, their reasoning, and how they reconcile the differences between their predictions and observations.

Idea Maps

Idea maps (also called context maps, semantic maps, concept maps, mind maps, or webs) provide insight into how students connect ideas together or how they see the structure of a whole topic. Of course, you first need to teach students how to make the maps, which can be done through modeling and practice examples.

Idea maps consist of two components, ideas and the interconnections among them. Each idea, usually expressed as a noun, is written within its own small oval (e.g., life cycle, metamorphosis, egg, larva, pupa, adult). The ovals that contain the ideas are interconnected by lines labeled with a verb or verb phrase (e.g., the line connecting "life cycle" and "metamorphosis" could be labeled "called", the line connecting "metamorphosis" and "eggs" could be labeled "starts with"). Arrows can be added at the ends of the connecting lines to show the direction of the connection (e.g., the line connecting "life cycle" and "metamorphosis" would point both ways, while the line connecting "metamorphosis" and "eggs" would point from "metamorphosis" to "eggs").

Figure 6.2 shows an idea map on the behaviour of light.

Figure 6.2

Idea Map: Behavior of Light

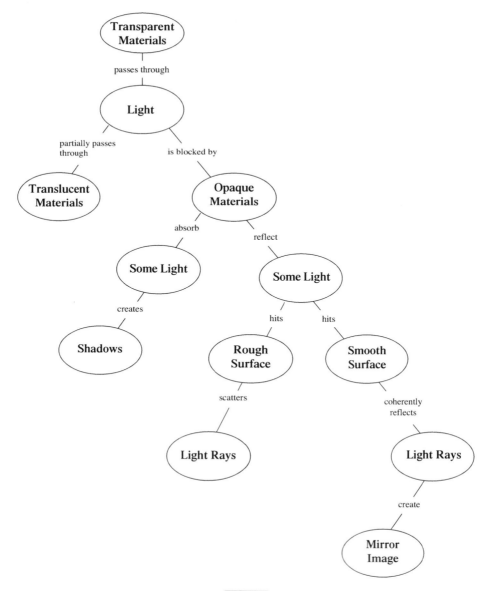

The number and selection of ideas, the variety and types of connections, the amount of detail in the map, and the clarity of the map structure can all give you insight into students' understandings. Idea maps can also show growth over time. You can compare before and after maps, or, as you work through the unit, students can re-visit their initial maps and add new ideas using a different color of ink or pencil crayon. Commercial computer software is available for making idea maps.

Drawings and Diagrams

Drawings and diagrams allow students to express their ideas visually and may reveal understandings that cannot be expressed by written and verbal responses. Most students like to draw and all that is required is to de-emphasize artistic performance and provide encouragement. Drawings can be of visible (e.g., plants) as well as invisible objects (e.g., molecules) and can be concrete or abstract in style. A set or series of drawings (e.g., growth of a plant over time) provides better insight into children's thinking than a single sketch. Pupils should include labels and explanations and can also be interviewed about their drawings.

Drawings made before, during, and after teaching help assess how much children's understanding has changed in the desired direction. For example, in scientific inquiry, children could draw their conception of an insect life cycle before, during, and after teaching. In technological problem-solving, drawing could be used to encourage children to express their design plans through three types of drawings: quick initial sketches, a series of refining and elaboration drawings, and a final presentation drawing of the completed product (see Chapter 2).

The following questions can be used to assess drawings:

- How does the child perceive what is being represented?
- What details are included in or omitted from the drawing?
- What information does the drawing convey?
- What information do the labels on the drawing convey?
- How does the child explain the drawing?

(Go to your Companion Manual, Textbook Activity 6.4 and think about the advantages and disadvantage of three different methods of evaluation.)

Portfolios

Portfolios are systematic, purposeful, and meaningful collections of samples of students' work that reflect the day-to-day learning activities of students. Both teachers and children should select the work that goes into portfolios. Portfolios are an effective form of assessment because they:

- Contain actual samples of children's work.
- Combine multiple and diverse types of materials (e.g., surveys, daily work records, idea maps, experimental write-ups, reflections, exams, and drawings).
- Contain a variety of work samples over an extended period of time thus comprehensively documenting student growth.
- Allow teachers to assess a broad range of concepts, skills, and attitudes.
- Communicate student progress to teachers, parents, and others, along with the evidence that the assessment of progress is based on.
- Provide students with opportunities to reflect on their own work.

Portfolio assessment may require a considerable time investment by the teacher if each work sample is evaluated in a different way. You will find it helpful to use a rubric because if the criteria of the evaluation are specifically defined in a single rubric each sample of work can be compared to the same rubric and scored on that basis. You should communicate the general parameters of the evaluation criteria to the students in advance so that they know what they are required to do.

Products of Practical Work

Both scientific inquiry and technological problem-solving provide opportunities for students to create concrete products that provide insights into their knowledge, skills, and attitudes. Examples include drawings, posters, displays, presentations, demonstrations, models, and inventions. Students should document the thinking that led to the creation of their products since you will not be able to monitor all phases of their work. Practical products on display in the classroom also provide a good opportunity to assess students' ability to communicate about their work to others.

Since technological problem-solving is product-based by nature, sometimes it is tempting to focus assessment solely on the purposeful products that the children have constructed. Although the product is important, this singular focus fails to capture the 'thinking in action' that gave rise to the product. Technological problem-solving assessments should also be designed to gain insight into the concepts, skill, and attitudes that develop as students participate in the thinking, designing, modeling, making, and evaluating that give rise to the final product.

Should you wish to assess the product of technological problem-solving, the following criteria provide a useful framework:

- **Purpose:** Does it fulfill the intended purpose? Did it solve the problem?
- **Materials:** Was it economically made with available materials?
- **Effort:** Was it easy to construct?
- **Effectiveness:** Does it work?
- **Reliability:** Does it work every time?
- **Durability:** Does it stand up to repeated use?
- **Safety:** Are there any risks involved in making it or using it?

Performance Assessment

In a performance assessment, students individually or in small groups perform a materials-based task that asks them to apply their learning to a new context. The task could be carrying out an experiment (fair test), designing and making a purposeful product, improving an existing design, solving a science or technology-related problem, or thinking critically about an STS issue. A performance assessment has three main components: student task, response record, and evaluation criteria.

To set the task, students are provided with concrete materials and instructions regarding what it is they are expected to do or find out. The materials provide a context for the problem, limit the number of possible solutions, and suggest pathways that may help students successfully complete the task. If you wish, you can provide extra materials and ask students to choose what they need. The task should allow many different solution paths that are equally appropriate and the students should be challenged to find one that is reasonable and effective. The student's performance is evaluated in terms of both the methods used and the final outcomes. Figure 6.3 provides an example of a performance task.

Figure 6.3
Sample Performance Task

Devise and carry out a fair test to answer the following question:

In a second class lever, how does the location of the fulcrum (F) affect the amount of effort (E) required to lift the load (L)?

Materials:

- **Lever:** Piece of wood, about 1 meter long, 7 cm wide, and 1 cm thick. The wood is grooved underneath at each and at the 25 cm, 50 cm, and 75 cm marks lengthwise. A screw eye is inserted into the middle of one end of the wood.
- **Fulcrum:** Triangular block of wood, 6 cm wide, 3 cm high
- **Load:** 100 gm weight
- Spring scale
- Ruler

The accompanying response record provides a means by which students can communicate their thinking and findings. The requested responses might include predictions, plans, alternative designs, lists of procedures, answers to questions, data charts, graphs, various kinds of evidence, drawings, diagrams,

Figure 6.4
Sample Response Record

1. Draw a diagram of how you will set up the materials to answer the question.
2. Explain how your set-up is testing a second class lever and not a first class lever.
3. List the steps in the procedure you will follow to gather your data.
4. How is your procedure designed to ensure that the test you are doing is a fair test?
5. Make a chart of your data.
6. What can you infer from your data chart about how the fulcrum's location affects the amount of effort required to lift the load?
7. What data from your chart supports the inference you made in response to Question 6 (above)?
8. How could what you found out be applied in everyday life to make your work easier? Give two examples.

hypotheses, explanations, recommended actions, reflections, suggested improvements, and self-evaluations. Students might also be asked to decide how to record their responses. Figure 6.4 shows a sample response record for the task described in Figure 6.3

Your evaluation criteria define what counts as an appropriate response and provide you with feedback about what students know and can do. The criteria need to take into consideration the various solution paths that students might follow since there will be many equally acceptable ways to complete the task. The evaluation criteria need to provide scope for student creativity but must also reflect that some solution paths are more reasonable or efficient than others. The criteria must also be reliable so that teachers scoring independently come up with similar student scores, and the criteria should be quick and easy to use. Rubrics are very useful for assessing performance tasks. Table 6.6 shows a rubric that could be used to assess the performance assessment.

Table 6.6

Performance Evaluation Rubric

Criterion	Level One	Level Two	Level Three	Level Four
Diagram of Set-up	Set up is not a lever of any class.	Set-up is a first class or third-class lever.	Set-up is a second class lever (Effort–Load–Fulcrum).	Set-up is a second class lever. Effort is directed upward.
Second-class Lever	Statement refers to positioning of only one of the load, fulcrum, or effort.	Statement refers to positioning of two of the load, fulcrum, and effort.	States that set-up is a second class lever because load is between fulcrum and effort.	States that load is between fulcrum and effort. In a first-class lever fulcrum is between load and effort.
Procedure Followed	Measurements are taken but locations of fulcrum and load are not controlled.	Measurements are taken but location of only one of fulcrum or load is controlled.	Measurements are taken with fulcrum at minimum 3 locations and load controlled at one location.	Two sets of measurements are taken with fulcrum at minimum 3 locations and load controlled at two different locations.
Fair Test	Is a fair test because one key variable is controlled (location of effort, fulcrum, load).	Is a fair test because two key variables are controlled (locations of two of effort, fulcrum, load).	Is a fair test because three key variables are controlled (locations of effort, fulcrum, and load).	Is a fair test because locations of effort, fulcrum, and load are controlled. Explanation is given of why this makes it a fair test.
Data Chart	Effort is measured with load at two or fewer locations and fulcrum at one location.	Effort is measured with load at three or more locations and fulcrum at one location, but data does not show pattern that effort decreases as fulcrum moves closer to load.	Effort is measured with load at three or more locations and fulcrum at one location. Data shows pattern that effort decreases as fulcrum moves closer to load.	Effort is measured with load at three or more locations and fulcrum at two different locations. Data shows pattern that effort decreases as fulcrum moves closer to load.
Relationship inferred from data patterns	The effect on the effort of the distance between the fulcrum and the load is not referred to.	The effect on the effort of the distance between the fulcrum and the load is referred to but an erroneous relationship is drawn.	Reference is made to the finding that less effort is required when the fulcrum is closer to the load.	Less effort is required when the fulcrum is closer to the load. More effort is required when the fulcrum is further from the load.
Data used to support inference	No data from chart is provided.	Data is provided but the data does not support the claim that the closer the load is to the fulcrum the less effort force is required.	One example of data is provided that supports the claim that the closer the load is to the fulcrum the less effort force is required.	Two examples of data are provided that support the claim that the closer the load is to the fulcrum the less effort force is required.
Everyday Application	Example(s) given do not illustrate that the closer the load is to the fulcrum the less effort force is required.	One example illustrates that the closer the load is to the fulcrum the less effort force is required. E.g., a load in a wheelbarrow should be placed above the wheel.	A second example illustrates that the closer the load is to the fulcrum the less effort force is required. E.g., the bracket for the oar of a rowboat should be closer to the flat end of the oar.	Two examples illustrate that the closer the load is to the fulcrum the less effort force is required. Explanation is given in at least one example as to how the example supports the claim.

Your evaluation criteria define what counts as an appropriate response and provide you with feedback about what students know and can do. The criteria need to take into consideration the various solution paths that students might follow since there will be many equally acceptable ways to complete the task. The evaluation criteria need to provide scope for student creativity but must also reflect that some solution paths are more reasonable or efficient than others. The criteria must also be reliable so that teachers scoring independently come up with similar student scores, and the criteria should be quick and easy to use. Rubrics are very useful for assessing performance tasks. Table 6.6 shows a rubric that could be used to assess the performance assessment.

Paper and Pencil Tests

The most common type of written feedback obtained by teachers after teaching is responses to questions on teacher-generated paper and pencil tests. Your tests should be authentic and require students to respond to open-ended questions, to make connections between concepts and lessons, and to involve students in relating school work to real world applications. They should allow children to display their thinking rather than just their ability to memorize. The types of test items that students are usually asked to respond to can be divided into two main groups: selection items, which provide a set of responses to select from, and supply items, which require significant student input.

The two main types of selection items are multiple choice and matching. Multiple choice items are made up of a question stem and usually four possible responses of which the student must select the best one. Multiple choice items can evaluate different levels of learning, can be reliable, can test a large knowledge base in a short time, and are easy to score. They are also difficult to write and are somewhat subject to guessing since students know that one of the choices is the desired response. Tips for writing good multiple choice items include:

- Test only for significant material.
- Base each item on a single learning goal.
- Keep items independent of one another.
- Phrase items using vocabulary at the students' level and ensure the wording of the question stem is clear.
- Ensure there is only one best response but make other possible responses plausible.
- Keep the lengths of the possible responses similar.

Matching items are the other main type of selection item and are made up of two sets of words or phrases that must be matched with each other (e.g., names of processes and their descriptions or key terms and their definitions). Students must unscramble the given order to match the two sets. Matching items are good for testing associations, can test complex items, and are quite objective. They are also difficult to write and are subject to the process of elimination.

Supply items are of two main kinds, short answer and long answer. Short answer items can test many ideas in a short time and are easy to score. They are difficult to use to measure complex learning and are sometimes ambiguous. Long answer items require a more lengthy written response so students' writing capabilities play a major role in how well they answer. Long answer items can test more complex learning but they are hard to score, require a lengthy testing time, and tend to be subjective.

Written tests can also be divided into teacher-made and standardized tests, with the latter almost always consisting of multiple choice test items. Traditionally most tests were teacher-made but standardized testing has increased in frequency and prominence, partially because of the growing focus on teacher accountability. Table 6.7 shows that standardized and teacher-made tests have advantages and disadvantages.

Written standardized achievement tests have been criticized as being neither fair not authentic because they (Kohn, 2000):

- Imply an unwarranted level of assessment objectivity.
- Misrepresent how human ability is assessed in the real world (e.g., workplace ability is usually measured by job performance not written responses).
- Primarily assess students' ability to retain facts in short-term memory and neglect more important learning (e.g., application, problem-solving, and critical thinking).
- Emphasize how students achieve in relation to each other (norm-referenced) rather than in relation to what they are supposed to learn (criterion-referenced) or to how well they progress (self-referenced).
- Must include what students would not be expected to know in order to create a range of scores among students.
- Discriminate against students and schools with fewer resources (e.g., small schools, low socioeconomic status, high numbers of ESL students, poor rural schools).

Table 6.7

Standardized and Teacher-Made Tests: Advantages and Disadvantages.

Standardized Tests	Teacher-Made Tests
Are more reliable. May be less valid.	Are less reliable. May be more valid.
Do not require teacher construction.	Take teacher time to construct.
Include norms for comparing with other classes and individuals.	Are based on classroom norms.
May not measure what is taught in the classroom.	Usually measure what is taught in the classroom.
Are expensive to administer.	Are inexpensive to administer.

- Cause high levels of anxiety and foster unhealthy competition among students and teachers.
- Are inappropriate for young learners.
- Take up too much time that could be more usefully spent teaching and learning.

(Go to your Companion Manual, Textbook Activity 6.5 and think about the issue of merit pay for teachers that is based on student achievement test scores.)

Assessing Skills and Attitudes

When teachers involve students in science and technology, they have in mind certain knowledge, skills, and attitudes they intend the experiences to foster. Traditional assessment has focused mainly on knowledge goals so it is useful to pay special attention to the assessment of skills and attitudes (See Chapter 3). In a hands-on, minds-on science and technology program, knowledge, skills, and attitudes are bound together and tend to be assessed together within the same activities. There are, however, assessment methods that are appropriate to each. The main method for assessing skills is observing children while they participate in an activity. You can collect information using a checklist, rating scale, or anecdotal records. Additionally, information about skill development can be observed in journals and can be probed using more formal methods of assessment.

Assessing Skills in Scientific Inquiry

Examples of some of the criteria that can be used for assessing scientific inquiry skills include:

OBSERVING

- Appropriately using several senses to explore objects and materials.
- Distinguishing relevant observations from irrelevant observations.
- Extending the senses using a hand lens or microscope as necessary.

COMMUNICATING

- Talking freely about activities and ideas.
- Listening to others' ideas and viewing their results.
- Using tables, graphs, and charts to record and report results.

EXPLAINING

- Trying to give an explanation that is consistent with evidence.
- Showing awareness there may be more than one explanation that fits the evidence.
- Showing awareness that all explanations are tentative and never totally proven.

PREDICTING

- Attempting to make a prediction relating to a problem.
- Gathering some of the evidence used in making a prediction.
- Explaining how evidence has been used in making predictions.

EXPERIMENTING (FAIR TESTING)

- Recognizing questions that can be experimentally investigated.
- Identifying the important variables involved in fair testing.
- Conducting fair tests in which a single variable is manipulated.

Assessing Skills in Technological Problem–Solving

Examples of some of the criteria that can be used for assessing technological problem-solving skills include:

PROPOSING A SOLUTION

- Selecting and using 2D and 3D approaches to planning and designing as appropriate.
- Carefully planning materials to ensure accuracy and avoid waste.
- Developing and detailing design ideas to the stage where they will work and can be made.

USING KNOWLEDGE OF MAKING

- Using knowledge of making as a springboard for design ideas.
- Using knowledge of making to evaluate and support decision making as design ideas are developed.
- Working out manufacturing issues before starting to build (e.g., types and amounts of materials, methods of shaping, joining, and finishing).

IMPLEMENTING A PROPOSED SOLUTION

- Choosing and using materials and tools appropriately to produce good quality outcomes.
- Constantly considering alternative solutions and ways of working.
- Compromising and optimizing to achieve an effective outcome.

EVALUATING A PRODUCT OR DESIGN

- Identifying clear criteria for judgments.
- Conducting evaluations of the product success against the design criteria.
- Talking about the positive and negative attributes of the purposeful product.

COMMUNICATING

- Discussing with others ways of overcoming problems.
- Commenting on own work and the work of others as it progresses.
- Using notes and drawings to communicate the thinking behind the purposeful product.

Assessing Skills in STS Decision-Making

Examples of some of the criteria that can be used for assessing STS decision-making skills include:

UNDERSTANDING THE ISSUE

- Locating science, technology, and society information related to the issue.

- Using a variety of sources to search for information.
- Assessing the reliability of information sources.

IDENTIFYING ALTERNATIVES

- Identifying relevant interest groups (stakeholders).
- Identifying the potential consequences of alternative courses of action.
- Considering scientific and technological knowledge that might help decide what action to take.

ANALYZING AND SYNTHESIZING INFORMATION

- Comparing and contrasting different points of view.
- Identify the perspectives of relevant stakeholder groups.
- Identifying the potential consequences of different courses of action.

Assessing Attitudes in Scientific Inquiry, Technological Problem–Solving, and STS Decision–Making

Specific attitudes can also be observed and recorded using checklists, rating scales, or anecdotal records. Examples of some of the criteria that can be used for assessing attitudes in scientific inquiry include:

SHOWING CURIOSITY ABOUT THE NATURAL WORLD

- Using several senses to explore objects and events.
- Asking questions about objects and events, materials, and methods.
- Actively investigating questions, problems, and methods.

RESPECT FOR EVIDENCE

- Using evidence to justify conclusions.
- Justifying designs and methods in terms of past experience.
- Changing ideas in response to evidence or logical reasons.

DISPLAYING OPEN-MINDEDNESS

- Showing respect for other ideas.
- Showing willingness to have own ideas questioned.
- Demonstrating willingness to modify ideas.

Examples of some of the criteria that can be used for assessing attitudes in technological problem-solving include:

SHOWING CONFIDENCE IN TECHNOLOGICAL ABILITIES

- Independently commencing the designing or imaging process.
- Providing assistance to others.
- Independently researching and working on personal questions.

DISPLAYING INVENTIVENESS

- Using materials and equipment in original and constructive ways.
- Deriving novel conclusions from observations.
- Suggesting new designs, methods, or applications.

TAKING PERSONAL RESPONSIBILITY

- Stating benefits to be gained from shared effort and cooperation.
- Being unwilling to blame other group members for apparent failure.
- Stating own responsibility within the group.

Examples of some of the criteria that can be used for assessing attitudes in STS decision-making include:

BEING RESPONSIBLE TOWARDS THE COMMUNITY

- Taking into account that personal choices and actions impact on the larger community.
- Surveying the opinions of community members in relation to an issue.
- Taking actions that show consideration for the feelings of community members.

RESPECTING THE OPINIONS OF OTHERS

- Ensuring that every member of a group has an opportunity to present opinions.
- Listening to and identifying a diversity of opinions.
- Considering other opinions with respect to your own.

Examples of some of the criteria that can be used for assessing attitudes common to scientific inquiry, technological problem-solving, and STS decision-making include:

SHOWING PERSEVERANCE

- Continuing to investigate after the novelty has worn off.
- Repeating an activity in spite of apparent failure.
- Completing an activity even though others have finished earlier.

BEING WILLING TO WORK WITH OTHERS

- Respecting others' ideas.
- Showing a willingness to modify own ideas.
- Sharing tasks in an equitable manner.

Self-Evaluation

Student Self-Evaluation

Student self-evaluation or reflection gives students the opportunity to step back from their work and think about why they do what they do. Students need to be encouraged to consider their work carefully, draw new insights and ideas, examine the many steps, choices, and decisions that guided them, and suggest alternative paths. In this way they take responsibility for carefully evaluating their own growth and development and become thoughtful judges of their own work. Through self-evaluation, students learn how to build on their strengths, and diagnose and improve their weaknesses.

Students can carry out self-evaluation in many different ways:

- Keeping logs of their daily progress.
- Reporting and describing what they did.
- Recording comments and thoughts about their decisions and choices.
- Engaging in classroom sharing of their work.
- Pondering possible strategies for improvement.
- Participating in peer response sessions and interviews.
- Writing formal reflections.

Teacher Self-Evaluation

Teachers should engage in ongoing self-evaluation, including consulting with peers and eliciting feedback from students. You can use a checklist such as the one found in Figure 6.5 to help you monitor your own teaching.

Another useful framework for teacher self-evaluation focuses on how often students do the following in the classroom (adapted from Harlen & Osborne,1985):

- Work on their own questions or problems.
- Define clearly what they are attempting to find out, investigate, and observe.
- Decide the best way of recording their ideas.
- Try out and discuss their observations and ideas with others.

- Base their statements on evidence, seek evidence to support statements, and confirm their findings carefully before accepting them as evidence.
- Seek out and interact with the ideas of others.
- Relate new ideas to previous ideas and experiences.
- Construct explanations and ideas.
- Devise and try out fair tests of their own and others' ideas.
- Reflect upon how they have tested ideas and how their testing can be improved.
- Base their conclusions on evidence and appreciate the tentative nature of conclusions.
- Are prepared to change their ideas in light of the evidence.

Grading and Reporting

Regular grading and reporting is required in every elementary classroom, including reporting on progress in science and technology learning. Grading is perceived to fulfill the following functions:

- Provide feedback to parents, students, and administrators about student progress and ability.
- Hold the teacher, students, and the school accountable for their actions.
- Improve learning by representing students' areas of strength as well as identifying their areas of weakness.
- Reward achievement and effort and stimulate further achievement.

School and district policies determine how students' grades are reported. Grades may be in a variety of symbolic forms, including letters (e.g., A, B, C, D), numbers (e.g., percentages), pass or fail, anecdotal comments, or a checklist of objectives to be met. Reported grades need to be backed up by evidence accumulated from a variety of assessments. Parents, in particular, may wish to look at the evidence. Since reported grades are a composite of different assessment components they may require complex calculations. One difficult problem for the teacher lies in determining the weighting of each component that contributes to the reported grade.

Grades are recorded on a report card that includes information on pupil progress in all three areas of knowledge, skill, and attitudes. Report cards can be lengthy and detailed, and may include accompanying comments and checklists, so teachers often need to put

Figure 6.5
Teacher Self-Evaluation.

___ I feel confident about my knowledge and ability to teach science and technology.

___ I conduct science and technology lessons regularly.

___ I am familiar with a variety of science and technology resources.

___ My lessons provide active, thinking experiences for students.

___ I provide sufficient time to complete lesson tasks.

___ My science and technology lessons have a recognizable structure.

___ I explain the purpose of the lesson and provide expectations.

___ I assist less able students and have higher expectations of more able students.

___ I am involved in the lesson at all times, including during student group work.

___ I structure discussions, direct questions to all, acknowledge contributions, and summarize.

___ I ask students to clarify or elaborate on their responses and to react to responses of others.

___ I provide constructive feedback on student responses.

___ I continually evaluate all aspects of work carried out by students.

(Adapted from Tobin & Fraser, 1999)

considerable time and energy investment into creating them. Report cards are given to students to be shown to parents and their distribution is usually followed by a parent-teacher conference at which the student may or may not be present. Talking constructively with parents about their children's grades can require considerable teacher knowledge and skill.

Reporting student progress in the form of grades is criticized on a number of grounds:

- It is difficult to establish an appropriate referent for grades.
- No approach to grading seems completely fair.
- Grades and grading systems are subject to a variety of interpretations.
- Students become motivated by grades instead of by learning.

- Reliability of grading is influenced by factors such as appearance, attitude, and gender.
- Grading causes anxiety, low self-esteem, and negative attitudes toward learning.

(Go to your Companion Manual, Textbook Activity 6.6 and think about how to discuss grading issues with parents.)

Summary Ideas

This chapter discusses the role assessment plays in science and technology education. The chapter presents some current thinking about:

- *What assessment is and the conditions needed to enhance students' opportunity to learn.* Assessment is an information–gathering process that encompasses all activities in which students are asked to demonstrate what they understand, know, and can do. Students' opportunities to learn are enhanced by the teacher's knowledge, the coordination between teaching and assessment, and available time and teaching resources.

- *Some common assessment terminology.* Common terminology includes ways of expressing the purpose and timing of the assessment, the manner in which the students' work will be judged, the dependability of the strategy, and the source of the assessment.

- *Fair and authentic assessment.* Fair assessment includes reviewing assessment instruments for their use of stereotypes, offensive language, gender and racial inclusiveness, and ability to accommodate the needs of diverse students. Authentic assessment encompasses a wide range of assessment strategies that are judged as realistic, practical, and aligned with instruction.

- *Thinking about assessment.* Teachers need to think about the purpose of gathering assessment information, design strategies to gather that information, make judgments about students' work, and use results to make decisions about future teaching and learning.

- *Assessment before teaching.* Teachers need to assess children's understanding prior to teaching them to find out the ideas they bring to lessons and to provide guidelines for teaching. Methods of assessment include interviews about events and concepts, surveys, predictions and plans, and pretests.

- *Formative assessment.* Teachers need to assess children's understanding during teaching them to find out what the children are making of the teaching and so that teaching can be changed in response to information gathered. Methods of assessment include observation checklists and rating scales, anecdotal records, questioning, daily classroom talk, and daily written work records.

- *Summative assessment after teaching.* Teachers need to assess children's understanding after teaching to find out how children have progressed and to inform future teaching. Methods of assessment include conferencing, predict-observe-explain (POE), idea maps, drawings and diagrams, portfolios, products of practical work, performance-based tasks, and paper and pencil tests.

- *Assessing skills and attitudes.* Traditional assessment focuses mainly on conceptual knowledge. It is also important to assess progress in developing appropriate skills and attitudes such as observation and open-mindedness.

- *Self-evaluation.* It is important that both students and teachers evaluate their own progress in order to develop reflective practice. Regular self-reflection helps pupils improve their work and teachers improve their teaching.

- *Reporting.* Teachers are required to report the results of their assessments to parents, children, and administrators. Reporting is a complex task that requires hard work on the part of the teacher, as well as effective use of assessment strategies during each reporting period.

Making Productive Connections

Scenario 1

You have just been hired to teach Grade 4. Your first science unit for the year is *Light and Shadows*. What plans would you make to ensure that your assessment in the unit is both fair and authentic?

Scenario 2

You have just been hired as a Grade 1 teacher. The principal asks you to prepare a comprehensive rubric for the evaluation of the *Building Things* unit that you will be teaching in your classroom. What specific knowledge, skill, and attitude outcomes are you going to assess? How will you assess those outcomes? How will you use the feedback from your assessments?

Ideas to Think About When Teaching Science, Technology, and Society

- How do I use assessment to help understand my students' conceptual understanding, skill, and attitude development?
- How do I share my philosophy of assessment with parents?
- How do I ensure that my assessment is both fair and authentic?
- What outcomes does my teaching focus on?
- How do I assess my outcomes?
- What assessment strategies do I use?
- When and in what forms do I obtain my assessment evidence?
- How do I use my assessment information to improve teaching and learning?
- How do I process my assessment information so it can be used to report pupil progress?

Selected Readings

Carlson, M.O., Humphrey, G.E., & Reinhart, K.S. (2003). *Weaving Science Inquiry and Continuous Assessment: Using Formative Assessment to Improve Learning.* Thousand Oaks, CA: Corwin Press.

The authors discuss the importance of continuous (formative) assessment for science teachers and how continuous assessment can be used in conjunction with science inquiry teaching.

Enger, S., & Yager, R. (2001). *Assessing Student Understanding in Science: A Standards-Based K-12 Handbook.* Thousand Oaks CA: Corwin Press.

This book offers numerous practical instruments for assessing student progress.

Kimbell, R., Stables, K., & Green, R. (1996). *Understanding Practice in Design and Technology.* Buckingham: Open University Press.

This book provides extensive discussion of the teaching, learning, and assessment of technological problem-solving.

Montgomery, K. (2001). *Authentic Assessment: A Guide for Elementary Teachers.* New York: Longman.

The author discusses theoretical ideas behind authentic assessment and illustrates how rubrics, portfolios, and self-assessment can be used to enhance assessment practice.

National Research Council (2001). *Classroom Assessment and the National Science Education Standards.* (Edited by J. M. Atkin, P. Black, & J. Coffey). Washington, D.C.: National Academy Press.

The authors focus on formative, classroom assessment and how to adjust science lessons based on information collected from the students.

Selected Websites

CENTER FOR THE ASSESSMENT AND EVALUATION OF STUDENT LEARNING
http://www.edgateway.net/cs/caesl/print/docs/179
This website provides information about quality classroom assessment practices.

GOVERNMENT OF UNITED KINGDOM
http://www.edu.dudley.gov.uk/technology/Advisory-page-strands.html
This website provides a comprehensive generic rubric for assessing technological problem-solving from a British perspective.

NATIONAL DIRECTORY
http://www.nationaldirectory.com/Science/Educational_Resources/Assessment
The website provides links to a wide variety of resources on science assessment.

NORTHWEST REGIONAL EDUCATIONAL LABORATORY
http://www.nwrel.org/assessment/pdfLibrary/science.pdf
This website provides a lengthy bibliography of articles on alternative science assessment.

PERFORMANCE ASSESSMENT LINKS IN SCIENCE
http://pals.sri.com/
This website provides information on performance assessment tasks appropriate to the NSE Standards (American).

Bibliography

Bibliography

AAAS (American Association for the Advancement of Science). (1964). *Science-A Process Approach.* Washington, DC: AAAS.

AAAS (American Association for the Advancement of Science). (1989). *Science for All Americans [Project 2061].* New York: Oxford University Press.

AAAS (American Association for the Advancement of Science). (1990). *The Liberal Art of Science: An Agenda for Action.* Washington, DC: AAAS.

AAAS (American Association for the Advancement of Science). (1993). *Project 2061: Benchmarks for Science Literacy.* New York: Oxford University Press.

AAAS (American Association for the Advancement of Science). (1994). *Project 2061: Science Literacy for a Changing Future: Update 1994.* Washington, DC: AAAS.

AAAS (American Association for the Advancement of Science). (1996). *Blueprints for Reform.* Washington, DC: AAAS.

AAAS (American Association for the Advancement of Science). (2000). *Designs for Science Literacy.* New York: Oxford University Press.

Abd-el-Khalick, F., Bell, R., Lederman, N. (1998). The nature of science and instructional practice: Making the unnatural natural. *Science Education, 82,* 417-436.

Aikenhead, G. (1996). Science education: Border crossing into the subculture of science. *Studies in Science Education, 27,* 1-52.

Airasian, P. (1994). *Classroom Assessment.* New York: McGraw-Hill.

Anderson, C., & Smith, E. (1987). Strategic teaching in science. In Jones, B., Palincsar, A., Ogle, D., Carr, E. (eds.), *Strategic Teaching and Learning; Cognitive Instruction in the Content Areas.* ASCD: Alexandria, VA.

Anning, A. (1994). Dilemmas and opportunities of a new curriculum: Design and technology with young children. *International Journal of Technology and Design Education, 4,* 155-177.

Anning, A. (1997). Teaching and learning how to design in schools. *Journal of Design and Technology Education, 2*(1), 50-52.

Appleton, K. (1997). *Teaching Science: Exploring the Issues.* Rockhampton, Australia: Central Queensland University Press.

Arellano, E.L., Barcenal, T.L., Bilbao, P.P., Castellano, M.A., Nichols, S. & Tippins, D.J. (2001). Case-based pedagogy as a context for collaborative inquiry in the Philippines. *Journal of Research in Science Teaching, 38*(5), 502-528.

Arnheim, R. (1969). *Visual Thinking.* Berkeley, CA: University of California Press.

Atkin J.M., & Karplus, R. (1962). Discovery or invention? *Science Teacher, 29*(5), 45.

Atwater, M.M. (1993). Multicultural science education. Assumptions and alternative views. *Science Teacher, 60*(3), 33-37.

Atwater, M.M. (1995). Multicultural science education, part I: Meeting the needs of a diverse student population. *Science Teacher, 62*(2), 21-23.

Atwater, M.M. (1995). Multicultural science classroom, part II: Assisting all students with science acquisition. *Science Teacher 62*(4), 42-45.

Atwater, M.M. (1995). Multicultural science classroom, part III: Preparing science teachers to meet the challenges of multicultural education. *Science Teacher, 62*(5), 26-29.

Ault, Jr., C. R. (1984, April). Intelligently wrong: Some comments on children's misconceptions. *Science and Children,* 22-24.

Ault, C. (1993). Technology as method-of-inquiry and six other (less valuable) ways to think about integrating technology and science in elementary education. *Journal of Science Teacher Education, 4*(2), 58-63.

Australia Curriculum Corporation. (1994). *Science: A Curriculum Profile for Australian Schools.* Carlton, Victoria: Australia.

Ausubel, D. (1968). *Educational Psychology: A Cognitive View.* New York: Holt, Rinehart, and Winston.

Ayers, H., Gray, F. (1998). *Classroom Management: A Practical Approach for Primary and Secondary Teachers.* London: D. Fulton.

Baker, D.R. (1998). Equity issues in science education. In B.J. Fraser and Tobin, K.G. (Eds.), *International Handbook of Science Education Part 2* (pp. 869-895), London: Kluwer Academic Publishers.

Banks, F. (Ed.). (1994). *Teaching Technology.* London: Routledge.

Barlax, D. (1991). Using science in design and technology. *Design and Technology Education, 23*(2), 148-151.

Barnes, D. (1976). *From Communication to Curriculum.* Harmondsworth: Penguin

Barnett J., & Hodson, D. (2001). Pedagogical context knowledge: Towards a fuller understanding of what good science teachers know. *Science Education, 85,* 426-453.

Belanoff, P. & Dickson, M. (1991). *Portfolios: Process and Product.* Portsmouth, NH: Heinemann.

Bennett, N., & Dunne, E. (1991). The nature and quality of talk in co-operative classroom groups. *Learning and Instruction, 1,* 103-118.

Black, P. & Wiliam, D. (1998). Inside the black box: Raising standards through classroom assessment. *Phi Delta Kappan, 80*(2), 139-148.

Bloom, B. (1956). *Taxonomy of Educational Objectives: Cognitive Domain.* New York: David McKay.

Bloom, J. (1998). *Creating a Classroom Community of Young Scientists.* Toronto: Irwin.

Boser, R.A. (1993). The development of problem solving capabilities in pre-service technology teacher education. *Journal of Technology Education, 4*(2), 12-29.

Bouillion, L., & Gomez, L.M. (2001). Connecting school and community with science learning: Real world problems and school-community partnerships as contextual scaffolds. *Journal of Research in Science Teaching, 38*(8), 878-898.

Bowers, B. (1989). Alternatives to standardized assessment. Eugene, OR: ERIC Clearinghouse on Educational Management (ERIC Document Reproduction Service No ED 312 773).

Bracey, G. (1993). Assessing the new assessments. *Principal, 72,* 34-36.

Brickhouse, N.W., Lowery, P., & Schultz, K. (2000). What kind of girl does science? The construction of school science identities. *Journal of Research in Science Teaching, 37*(5), 441-458.

Broadfoot, P. (1995). Performance assessment in perspective: international trends and current English experience. In H. Torrance (Ed.), *Evaluating Authentic Assessment* (pp. 9-43). Buckingham: Open University Press.

Brooks, J., & Brooks, M. (2001). *In Search of Understanding: The Case for Constructivist Classrooms.* Upper Saddle River, NJ: Prentice Hall.

Brown, J. R. (2001). *Who Rules in Science?* Cambridge MA: Harvard University Press.

Brown, J.S., Collins, A., & Duguid, P. (1989). Situated cognition and the culture of learning. *Educational Researcher, 18,* 32-42.

Bruner, J. (1962). *The Process of Education.* Cambridge, MA: Harvard University Press.

Bruner, J. (1962a). *On Knowing: Essays for the Left Hand.* Cambridge, MA: Harvard University Press.

Bruner, J. (1966). *Toward a Theory of Instruction.* Cambridge, MA: Harvard University Press.

Bucciarelli, L. (1999). *Designing Engineers.* Cambridge, MA: MIT Press.

Burden, P.R., & Byrd, D.M. (1998). *Methods for Effective Teaching (2nd edition).* Boston: Allyn and Bacon.

Burns, E. (2001). *Developing and Implementing IDEA-IEPs.* Springfield, IL: Charles C. Thomas.

Bybee, R.W. (1997). *Achieving Scientific Literacy: From Purposes to Practices.* Portsmouth, NH: Heinemann.

Bybee, R. (1994). *Reforming Science Education: Social Perspectives and Personal Reflections.* New York: Teachers College Press, Columbia University.

Bybee, R., Buchwald, C., Crissman, S., Heil, D., Kuerbis, P., Matsumoto, C, & McInerney, J. (1989). *Science and Technology Education for the Elementary Years: Frameworks for Curriculum and Instruction.* Washington DC: National Center for Improving Science Education.

Caccamise, F.C. & Lang, H.G. (1996). *Signs for Science and Mathematics: A Resource Book for Teachers and Students.* Rochester, NY: National Technical Institute for the Deaf.

Calabrese Barton, A. (2001). Science education in urban settings: Seeking new ways of praxis through critical ethnography. *Journal of Research in Science Teaching, 38*(8), 899-917.

Calabrese Barton, A., & Tobin, K. (2001). Preface. *Journal of Research in Science Teaching, 38*(8), 843-846.

Calabrese Barton, A., Tobin, K.G., & Gallagher, J.J. (2001). Preface. *Journal of Research in Science Teaching, 38*(9), 981-982.

Canter, L., & Canter, M. (1978). *Assertive Discipline: A Take Charge Approach for Today's Educator.* Seal Beach CA: Canter and Associates.

Carlsen, W.S. (1991). Questioning in classrooms: a sociolinguistic perspective. *Preview of Educational Research, 61*(2), 157-178.

Clewell, B.C., Anderson, B.T., & Thorpe, M.E. (1992). *Breaking the Barriers: Helping Female and Minority Students Succeed in Mathematics and Science.* San Francisco: Jossey-Bass.

Coburn, W.W., & Aikenhead, G.S. (1998). Cultural aspects of learning science. In B.J. Fraser and K.G. Tobin (Eds.), *International Handbook of Science Education Part I* (pp. 39-52), London: Kluwer Academic Publishers.

Collins, A. (1992). Portfolios: Questions for design. *Science Scope, 15*(6), 25-27.

Council of Ministers of Education, Canada (1997). *Common Framework of Science Learning Outcomes.* Toronto, ON: CMEC.

Craig, G.S. (1957). Elementary school science in the past century. *Science Education, 24*(4), 11-14.

Cross, N. (1989). *Engineering Design Methods.* New York: John Wiley & Sons.

Cross, N., & Clayburn Cross, A. (1998). Expertise in engineering design. *Research in Engineering Design, 10,* 141-149.

Custer, R.L. (1995). Examining the dimensions of technology. *International Journal of Technology and Design Education, 5*(5), 219-244.

Darling-Hammond, L., Ancess, J., & Falk, B. (1995). *Authentic Assessment in Action: Studies of Schools and Students at Work.* New York: Teachers College Press.

Dart, B., & Clarke, J. (1991). Helping students become better learners: A case study in teacher education. *Higher Education, 22*(3), 317-335.

Davies, D. (1996). Professional design and primary children. *International Journal of Technology and Design Education, 6*(1), 45-59.

Davies, D. (1997). The relationship between science and technology in the primary curriculum – Alternative perspectives. *Journal of Technology Education, 2*(2), 100-111.

Davies, F., & Greene, T. (1984). *Reading for Learning in the Sciences.* Edinburgh: Oliver and Boyd.

DeBoer, G. (1991). *A History of Ideas in Science Education: Implications for Practice.* New York: Teachers College Press.

Demers, C. (2000). Beyond paper and pencil assessments. *Science and Children, 38*(2), 24-29, 60.

Department for Education and Welsh Office Education Department. (1995). *Design and Technology in the National Curriculum.* London: HMSO.

Dove, J., Everett, L. & Preece, P. (1999). Exploring a hydrologic concept through children's drawings. *International Journal of Science Education, 21*(5), 485-497.

Dreikurs, R., & Cassell, P. (1980). *Discipline Without Tears.* New York: Hawthorn/Dutton Books.

Driver, R. (1983). *The Pupil as Scientist?* Open University Press.

Driver, R., Guesne, E., & Tiberghien, A. (Eds.). (1985). *Children's Ideas in Science.* Philadelphia, PA: Open University Press.

Driver, R., & Bell, B. (1986). Students' thinking and the learning of science: a constructivist view. *School Science Review, 67*(240), 443-456.

Driver, R. (1989). The construction of scientific knowledge in school classrooms. In R. Millar (Ed.), *Doing Science: Images of Science in Science Education.* London: Falmer Press.

Driver, R., Asoko, H., Leach, J., Mortimer, E., & Scott, P. (1994). Constructing scientific knowledge in the classroom. *Educational Researcher, 23*(7), 5-12.

Dunbar, R. (1995). *The Trouble With Science.* Cambridge MA: Harvard University Press.

Edelson, D.C. (2001). Learning-for-Use: A framework for the design of technology-supported inquiry activities. *Journal of Research in Science Teaching, 38*(3), 355-385.

Education Development Center. (1960). *Elementary Science Study.* Newton MA: EDC.

Eggleston, J. (1996). *Teaching Design and Technology (2nd edition).* Buckingham, UK: Open University Press.

Elstegeest, K. (1985). The right question at the right time. In W. Harlen (Ed.), *Primary Science: Taking the Plunge,* (pp. 34-36). London: Heinemann Educational Books.

Elstgeest, K. & Harlen, W. (1990). *Environmental Science in the Primary Curriculum.* London: Paul Chapman.

Etheredge, S., & Rudnitsky, A. (2003). *Introducing Students to Scientific Inquiry: How Do We Know What We Know?* Boston: Pearson Education.

Fazey, D. (1993). Self-assessment as a generic skill for enterprising students: The learning process. *Assessment and Evaluation in Higher Education, 18*(3), 235-250.

Fensham, P.J. (1988). Approaches to the teaching of STS in science education. *International Journal of Science Education 10*(4), 346-56.

Fensham, P.J. (1990). What will science education do about technology? *The Australian Science Teachers Journal, 36*(3), 8-21.

Fensham, P.J., Gunstone, R.F., & White, R.T. (Eds.) (1994). *The Content of Science: A Constructivist Approach to Its Teaching and Learning.* Bristol, PA: Falmer Press.

Fenstermacher, G. (1986). Philosophy of research on teaching: Three aspects. In M. Wittrock (Ed.), *Handbook of Research on Teaching* (3rd Ed.), New York: Macmillan.

Finley, F.N. (1983). Science processes. *Journal of Research in Science Teaching, 20*(1), 47-54.

Fleer, M. (1999). The science of technology: Young children working technologically. *International Journal of Technology and Design Education, 9,* 269-291.

Fleer, M. (2000). Working technologically: Investigations into how young children design and make during technology education. *International Journal of Technology and Design Education, 10,* 43-59.

Fusco, D. (2001). Creating relevant science through urban planning and gardening. *Journal of Research in Science Teaching, 38*(8), 860-877.

Gadd, T., & Morton, D. (1993). *Technology Key Stage 2.* UK: Stanley Thornes.

Gagne, R.M. (1965). *The Psychological Basis of Science – A Process Approach.* Washington, D.C.: AAAS.

Gagne, R.M. (1970). *The Conditions of Learning (2nd edition).* New York: Holt, Rinehart and Winston.

Gagne, R. (1975). *Essentials of Learning for Instruction.* New York: Holt, Rinehart, Winston.

Gagne, R.M., & Driscoll, M.P. (1988). *Essentials of Learning for Instruction (2nd edition).* Englewood Cliffs, NJ: Prentice-Hall.

Gallas, K. (1995). *Talking Their Way Into Science.* New York: Teachers College Press.

Gardner, H., & Hatch, T. (1989). Multiple intelligences go to school: educational implications of the theory of multiple intelligences. *Educational Researcher, 47*(7), 33-37.

Giangreco, M.F. (1998). *Quick-Guides to Inclusion 2: Ideas for Educating Students With Disabilities.* Baltimore, MD: Paul H. Brookes.

Gilbert, J.K. (1992). The interface between science education and technology education. *International Journal of Science Education, 14*(5), 563-578.

Gilbert, J.K. & Boulter, C.J. (2000). (Eds.). *Developing Models in Science Education.* Dordrecht: Kluwer Academic Publishers.

Gilbert, J.K., Boulter, C.J., & Elmer, R. (2000). Positioning models in science education and in design and technology education. In J.K. Gilbert & C.J. Boulter, (Eds.), *Developing Models in Science Education* (pp. 3-18). Dordrecht: Kluwer Academic Publishers.

Ginott, H. (1972). *Teacher and Child: A Book for Parents and Teachers.* New York: Macmillan.

Gipps, C. (1995). Reliability, validity, and manageability in large-scale performance assessment. In H. Torrance (Ed.), *Evaluating Authentic Assessment* (pp. 105-123), Buckingham: Open University Press.

Gipps, C., McCallum, B., & Hargreaves, E. (2000). *What Makes a Good Primary School Teacher?* London: Routledge Falmer.

Giroux, H. (1992). *Border Crossings: Cultural Workers and the Politics of Education.* NY: Routledge.

Glasser, W. (1998). *The Quality School: Managing Students Without Coercion.* New York: Harper Perennial.

Glynn, S., & Duit, R. (1995). *Learning Science in the Schools.* Mahwah NJ: Lawrence Erlbaum.

Gould, S. (1997). *Ever Since Darwin.* New York: W. W. Norton.

Green, T. (1968). *The Activities of Teaching*. New York: McGraw-Hill.

Gregg, T. (1993). The 'Greenhouse Effect': Children's perceptions of causes, consequences, and cures. *International Journal of Science Education, 15*(5), 531-552.

Haack, S. (2003). *Defending Science—Within Reason*. Amherst NY: Prometheus Books.

Habib, D. (1992). A multicultural approach to science education. *Connect, 6*(1), 3-5.

Hacking, I. (1999). *The Social Construction of What?* Cambridge MS: Harvard University Press.

Hammon, L. (2001). Notes from California: An anthropological approach to urban science education for language minority families. *Journal of Research in Science Teaching, 38*(9), 983-999.

Harding, P., & Hare, W. (2000). Portraying science accurately in classrooms: Emphasizing open-mindedness rather than relativism. *Journal of Research in Science Teaching, 37*(3), 225-36.

Harlan, J., & Rivkin, M. (2004). *Science Experiences for the Early Childhood Years; An Integrated Affective Approach*. 8th Edition. (2000). Upper Saddle River NJ: Merrill Prentice Hall.

Harlen, W. (1988). *The Teaching of Science*. London: Fulton.

Harlen, W. (Ed.) (1994). *Enhancing Quality in Assessment*. London: Paul Chapman Publishing.

Harlen, W. (2000). *Teaching, Learning and Assessing Science 5-12 (3rd edition)*. London: Paul Chapman.

Harlen, W. (2000a). The Teaching of Science in Primary Schools (3rd edition). London: David Fulton Publishers.

Harlen, W., Gipps., C., Broadfoot, P., & Nuttall, D. (1992). Assessment and the improvement of education. *Curriculum Journal, 3*(3), 215-230.

Harlen, W. & Jelly, S. (1989). *Developing Science in the Primary Classroom*. Essex: Oliver & Boyd.

Harre, R. (1984). *The Philosophies of Science*. Oxford: Oxford University Press.

Harris, J.W. (1995). Sheltered instruction: Bridging the language gap in the science classroom. *Science Teacher 62*(2), 24-27.

Hart, D. (1994). *Authentic Assessment: A Handbook for Educators*. Menlo Park, CA: Addison-Wesley Publishing Company.

Harwood, W.S., & McMahon, M.M. (1997). Effects of integrated video media on student achievement and attitudes in high school chemistry. *Journal of Research in Science Teaching, 34*, 617-631.

Hassard, J. (1992). *Minds On Science: Middle and Secondary School Methods*. NY: Harper Collins.

Hayes, D. (1994). Drawing during science activity in primary school. *International Journal of Science Education, 16*(3), 265-277.

Hempel, C.G. (1965). *Aspects of Scientific Explanation and Other Essays in the Philosophy of Science*. NY: The Free Press.

Hempel, C.G. (1966). *Philosophy of Natural Science*. Englewood Cliffs, NJ: Prentice-Hall.

Hennessy, S., and Murphy, P. (1999). The potential for collaborative problem solving in design and technology. *International Journal of Technology and Design Education, 9*, 1-36.

Hesse, M. (1966). *Models and Analogies in Science*. London: Sheen and Ward.

Hewitt, P. (1992). *Conceptual Physics*. Menlo Park CA: Addison Wesley.

Hewson, P.W., & Thorley, N.R. (1989). The conditions of conceptual change in the classroom. *International Journal of Science Education, 11*(5), 541-553.

Hodson, D. (1992). Assessment of practical work: Some considerations in philosophy of science. *Science and Education, 1*(2), 115-134.

Hodson, D. (1993). Re-thinking old ways: towards a more critical approach to practical work in school science. *Studies in Science Education, 22*, 85-142.

Hodson, D. (1993). In search of a rationale for multicultural science education. *Science Education, 77*(6), 685-711.

Hodson, D. (1999). Going beyond cultural pluralism: Science education for sociopolitical action. *Science Education, 83*(6), 775-796.

Hurd, P. (1998). Scientific literacy: New minds for a changing world. *Science Education 82*(3), 407-416.

International Technology Education Association (2000). *Standards for Technological Literacy: Content for the Study of Technology.* Reston, VA: ITEA.

Jarvis, T., & Rennie, L.J. (1996). Perceptions about technology held by primary teachers in England. *Research in Science and Technological Education, 14*(1), 43-54.

Jarvis, T., and Rennie, L. (1998). Factors that influence children's developing perceptions of technology. *International Journal of Technology and Design Education, 8*, 261-279.

Jenkins, E.W. (1990). Scientific literacy and school science education. *School Science Review, 71*(25), 43-51.

Jenkins, E.W. (1995). Benchmarks for scientific literacy: A review symposium. *Journal of Curriculum Studies, 27*(4), 445-461.

Jenkins, E.W. (1997). Technological literacy: Concepts and constructs. *Journal of Technology Studies, XXIII*, 2-5.

Johnsey, R. (1997). Improving children's performance in the procedures of design and technology. *Journal of Design and Technology, 2*(3), 201-207.

Jones, A. (1997a). An analysis of student existing technological framework capability: Developing an initial framework. *Mathematics and Technology Education Research, 7*, 241-258.

Jones, A. (1997b). Recent research in learning technological concepts and processes. *International Journal of Technology and Design Education, 7*, 83-96.

Kahle, J.B. (1985). Retention of girls in science: Case studies of secondary teachers. In J.B. Kahle (Ed.) *Women in Science: A Report From the Field* (pp. 49-76 & 193-229). London: Falmer Press.

Kahle, J.B. & Lakes, M.K. (1983). The myth of equality in science classrooms. *Journal of Research in Science Teaching, 20*, 131-140.

Kame'enui E.J., Carnin, D.W., Dixon, R.C., Simmons, D.C., & Coyne, M.D. (2002). *Effective Teaching Strategies That Accommodate Diverse Learners.* Upper Saddle River, NJ: Merrill Prentice Hall.

Karplus, R. (1964). The Science Curriculum Improvement Study—Report to the Piaget Conference. *Journal of Research in Science Teaching, 2*, 236-40.

Karplus, R., & Their, H. (1967). *A New Look at Elementary School Science: Science Curriculum Improvement Study.* Chicago: Rand McNally.

Kelly, A. (Ed.). (1981). *The Missing Half: Girls and Science Education.* Manchester: Manchester University Press.

Kelly, G. (1955). *The Psychology of Personal Constructs.* New York: W. W. Norton.

Kimbell, R. (1992). *Assessing technological capability.* Proceedings of the International Conference on Technology and Education (pp. 219-231). Weimar, Germany.

Kimbell, R. (1994). Progression in learning and the assessment of children's attainments in technology. *International Journal of Technology and Design Education, 4,* 65-83.

Kimbell, R. (1997). *Assessing Technology.* Buckingham: Open University Press.

King, A. (1994). Guiding knowledge construction in the classroom: effects of teaching children how to question and how to explain. *American Educational Research Journal, 31*(2), 338-368.

Kleinheider, J.K. (1996). Assessment matters. *Science and Children, 33*(4), 23-25, 41.

Kluger-Bell, B. (1995). T*he Exploratorium Guide to Scale and Structure.* Portsmouth, NH: Heinemann.

Koch, J. 1993). Face to face with science misconceptions. *Science and Children, 30*(3), 39-40.

Kohn, A. (2000). *The Case Against Standardized Testing: Raising the Scores, Ruining the Schools.* Portsmouth, NH: Heinemann.

Kolsto, S. (2001). Scientific literacy for citizenship: Tools for dealing with the science dimension of controversial socio-scientific issues. *Science Education, 85*(3), 291-310.

Kounin, J. (1977). *Discipline and Group Management in Classrooms.* Huntington NY: R.E. Krieger.

Krajcik, J., Czerniak, C., & Berger, C. (1999). *Teaching Children Science: A Project-based Approach.* New York: McGraw Hill.

Kuhn, D. (1993). Science as argument: Implications for teaching and learning scientific thinking. *Science Education, 77*(3), 319-337.

Kuhn, T.S. (1962). *The Structure of Scientific Revolutions.* Chicago, IL: University of Chicago Press. Kuhn, T.S. (1970). *The Structure of Scientific Revolutions (2nd edition).* Chicago: Chicago University Press.

Lang, H.G. & Propp, G. (1982). Science education for hearing impaired students: State of the art. *American Annals of the Deaf, 127,* 860-869.

Lang, H.G. (1994). *Silence of the Spheres: The Deaf Experience in the History of Science.* Bergin and Garvey Press.

Lang, H.G. & Albertini, J.A. (2001). The construction of meaning in the authentic writing of deaf students. *Journal of Deaf Studies and Deaf Education, 6,* 258-284.

Langer, J.A. (1986). Reading, writing, and understanding. *Written Communication, 3*(2), 219-267.

Layton, D. (1993). Knowing about other cultures. *Design and Technology Times,* Summer, 1993. Salford, UK: The University.

Layton, D. (1993). *Technology's Challenge to Science Education.* Buckingham: Open University Press.

Leahy, T., & Harris, R. (1997). *Learning and Cognition.* Upper Saddle River, NJ: Prentice Hall.

Lederman, N.G. (1992). Students' and teachers' conceptions of the nature of science: A review of research. *Journal of Research in Science Teaching, 29,* 331-359.

Lederman, N., Abd-el-Khalick, F., Bell, R., Schwartz, R (1998). Views of Nature of Science Questionnaire. Toward valid and meaningful assessment of learners' conceptions of nature of science. *Journal of Research in Science Teaching, 39* (6), 497-521.

Lemke, J. (1990). *Talking Science: Language Learning and Values.* Norwood NJ: Ablex Publishing.

Leplin, J. *Scientific Realism.* Berkley CA: University of California Press.

Levine, E.L. & Wexler, E.M. (1981). *PL 94-142 An Act of Congress*. NY: Macmillan.

Liem, Tik (1987). *Invitations to Inquiry* (2nd Edition). Chino Hills CA: Science Inquiry Enterprises.

Liftig, I., Liftig, B., & Eaker, B. (1992). Making assessment work: What teachers should know before they try it. *Science Scope, 15*, 4-6.

Lindstrom, M. (2002). Achieving technological literacy in Minnesota. *Technology Teacher, 61*(8), 16-20.

Linn, R.L. (1993). Educational assessment: expanded expectations and challenges. *Educational Evaluation and Policy Analysis, 15*(1), 1-16.

Lowery, L.F. (Ed.) (1997). *NSTA Pathways to the Science Standards: Elementary School Edition (2nd edition)*. Arlington, VA: NSTA Press.

Lynch, S. (2001). "Science for All" is not equal to "One Size Fits All": Linguistic and cultural diversity and science education reform. Journal of Research in Science Teaching, *38*(5), 622-627.

Martin, K., & Miller, E. (1988). Storytelling and science. *Language Arts, 65*(3), 255-59.

Matthews, M. (1998a). (Ed.) *Constructivism in Science Education*. Dordrecht: Kluwer.

Matthews, M. (1998b). In defense of modest goals when teaching about the nature of science. *Journal of Research in Science Teaching, 35*(2), 161-174.

Matthews, M. (1994). *Science Teaching: The Role of the History and Philosophy of Science*. New York: Routledge.

McCain, G., & Segal, E. (1969). *The Game of Science*. Belmont CA: Wadsworth.

McCormick, R. (1997). *Conceptual and Procedural Knowledge*. Paper presented at the Second Jerusalem International Science and Technology Conference on Technology Education for a Changing Future: Theory, Policy and Practice, Jerusalem.

McCormick, R., Hennessy, S., & Murphy, P. (1993). A pilot study of children's problem-solving processes. In J.S. Smith (Ed.), *Proceedings of the International Conference on Design and Technology Educational Research and Curriculum Development* (pp. 8-12). Loughborough, University of Loughborough.

Medawar, P. (1969). *Induction and Intuition in Scientific Thought*. London: Methuen.

Medway, P. (1994). The language component in technological capability: Lessons from architecture. *International Journal of Technology and Design Education, 4*, 85-107.

Meng, E., & Doran, R.L. (1990). What research says … about appropriate methods of assessment. *Science and Children, 28*(1), 42-45.

Metz, K.E. (1991). Development of explanation: Incremental and fundamental change in children's physics knowledge. *Journal of Research in Science Teaching, 28*(9), 785-797.

Millar, R. (1989a). Constructive criticisms. *International Journal of Science Education, 11*, 587-96.

Millar, R. (1989b). *Doing Science: Images of Science in Science Education*. London: Falmer Press.

Millar, R. & Driver, R. (1987). Beyond processes. *Studies in Science Education, 14*, 33-62.

Millar, R., & Osborne, J. (1998). *Beyond 2000 Science Education for the Future*. London: King's College London, School of Education.

Monk, M. & Osborne, J. (1997). Placing the history and philosophy of science on the curriculum: A model for the development of pedagogy. *Science Education, 81,* 405-424.

Munby, H., & Roberts, D. (1998). Intellectual independence: A potential link between science teaching and responsible citizenship. In D. Roberts & L. Ostman (Eds.), *Problems of Meaning in Science Curriculum* (pp. 101-114). New York: Teachers College Press.

Murphy, P., & McCormick, R. (1997). Problem solving in science and technology education. *Research in Science Education, 27*(3), 461-481.

National Association of Advisers and Inspectors in Design Technology. (1994). Quality and design and technology: What we should be looking for. *Design and Technology Teaching, 26*(2), 53-59.

National Commission on Excellence in Education. (1983). *A Nation at Risk: The Imperative for Educational Reform.* Washington, DC: US Government Printing Office.

National Research Council. (1996). *National Science Education Standards.* Washington, DC: National Academy Press.

National Research Council. (1999). *Selecting Instructional Materials.* Washington, DC: National Academy Press.

National Science Board Commission on Precollege Education in Mathematics, Science and Technology. (1983). *Educating Americans for the 21st Century.* Washington, DC: NSB.

National Science Foundation. (1992). *The Influence of Testing on Teaching Math and Science in Grades 4-12: Report of a Study.* Chestnut Hill, MA: Center for the Study of Testing, Evaluation, and Educational Policy.

National Science Resources Center. (1997). *Science For All Children: A Guide to Improving Elementary Science Education in Your School District.* Washington, DC: National Academy Press.

Newton, D. (2002). *Talking Sense in Science.* London: Routledge Falmer.

Newton, L., and Newton, D. (1998). Primary children's conceptions of science and the scientist: Is the impact of a National Curriculum breaking down the stereotype? *International Journal of Science Education, 20*(9), 1137-1149.

Norman, O., Ault, C.R., Bentz, B., & Meskimen, L. (2001). The black-white "Achievement Gap" as a perennial challenge of urban science education: A sociocultural and historical overview with implications for research and practice. *Journal of Research in Science Teaching, 38*(10), 1101-1114.

Norris, S.P., & Phillips, L.M. (1994). Interpreting pragmatic meaning when reading popular reports of science. *Journal of Research in Science Teaching, 31*(9), 947-967.

Novak, J. (1984). *Learning How to Learn.* Cambridge University Press.

Olson, S (Ed.) & Loucks-Horsley, S. (2000). *Inquiry and the National Science Education Standards: A Guide for Teaching and Learning.* Washington, DC: National Academy Press.

Orsolini, M., & Pontecorvo, C. (1992). Children's talk in classroom discussions. *Cognition and Instruction, 9*(2), 113-136.

Osborne, J. (1996). Beyond constructivism. *Science Education, 80*(1), 53-82.

Osborne, R. & Freyberg, P. (Eds.). (1985). *Learning in Science: The Implications of Children's Science.* NZ: Heinemann.

Osborne, R., & Wittrock, M. (1983). Learning science: a generative process. *Science Education, 67*(4), 489-508.

Pacey, A. (1983). *The Culture of Technology.* Oxford: Blackwell.

Pacey, A. (1990). *Technology in World Civilization: A Thousand-year History.* Cambridge, MA: MIT Press.

Pacey, A. (1999). *Meaning in Technology.* Cambridge, MA: MIT Press.

Parsons, K. (2003). *The Science Wars.* Amherst NY: Prometheus.

Phillips, D. (1984). *Philosophy, Science, and Social Inquiry.* Oxford: Pergamon Press.

Phillips, D. (1995). The good, the bad, and the ugly: The many faces of constructivism. *Educational Researcher, 24*(7), 5-12.

Phillips, D. (1997). Coming to grips with radical social constructivism. *Science & Education 6,* 85-104.

Piaget, J. (1929). *The Child's Conception of the World.* London: Kegan Paul, Trench, Taubner, & Co.

Piaget, J. (1926). *The Language and Thought of the Child.* London: Routledge and Kegan Paul.

Pomeroy, D. (1994). Science education and cultural diversity: Mapping the field. *Studies in Science Education, 24,* 49-73.

Posner, G., Strike, K., Hewson, P., & Gertzog, W. (1982). Accommodation of a scientific conception: towards a theory of conceptual change. *Science Education, 66*(2), 211-227

Raat, J., de Vries, M., & Mottier, I. (Eds.). (1995). Teaching technology for entrepreneurship and employment. *Pupil's Attitude Toward Technology (Report Proceedings PATT-7 Conference).* Western Cape, South Africa: Nasou-Via Afrika.

Raizen, S.A., Baron, J.B., Champagne, A.B., Haertel, E., Mullis, I.V., & Oakes, J. (1989). *Assessment in Elementary School Science Education.* Washington, DC: National Center for Improving Science Education.

Raizen, S.A., & Michelsohn, A.M. (Eds). (1994). *The Future of Science in Elementary Schools: Educating Prospective Teachers.* San Francisco: Jossey-Bass.

Rennie, L., & Jarvis, T. (1995). Children's choice of drawings to communicate their ideas about technology. *Research in Science and Technological Education, 13*(1), 37-52.

Richmond, G., & Striley, J. (1996). Making meaning in classrooms: Social processes in small-group discourse and scientific knowledge building. *Journal of Research in Science Teaching, 33*(8), 839-858.

Roberts, D.A. (1982). Developing the concept of "curriculum emphases" in science education. *Science Education, 66*(2), 243-260.

Roberts, D.A., & Ostman, L. (Eds.). (1998). *Problems of Meaning in Science Curriculum.* NY: Teachers College Press, Columbia University.

Roden, C. (1999). How children's problem solving strategies develop at Key Stage 1. *Journal of Design and Technology Education, 4*(1), 21-27.

Roden, C. (1997). Young children's problem-solving in design and technology: Towards a taxonomy of strategies. *Journal of Design and Technology Education, 2*(1), 14-19.

Rose, L.C., & Dugger, W.E. (2002). TEA/Gallup poll reveals what Americans think about technology. *Technology Teacher, 61*(6), 1-7.

Roth, W.-M. (1996). Teacher questioning in an open-inquiry learning environment: Interactions of context, content, and student responses. *Journal of Research in Science Teaching, 33*(7), 709-736.

Roth, W.-M. (1995). *Authentic School Science: Knowing and Learning in Open-inquiry Science Laboratories.* Boston, MA: Kluwer Academic Publishers.

Rowe, M.B. (1973). *Teaching as Continuous Inquiry.* New York, NY: McGraw-Hill.

Rutherford, F.J. (1964). The role of inquiry in science teaching. *Journal of Research in Science Teaching, 2,* 80-84.

Rutherford, F.J., & Ahlgren, A. (1989). *Science for All Americans.* NY: Oxford University Press.

Sagan, C. (1996). *The Demon-haunted World. Science as a Candle in the Dark.* New York, NY: Ballantine Books

Scheffler, I. (1960). *The Language of Education.* Springfield Il: Charles Thomas.

Scheffler, I. (1967). *Science and Subjectivity.* Indianapolis IN: Bobbs-Merrill.

Scheffler, I. (1973). *Reason and Teaching.* Indianapolis IN: Bobbs-Merrill.

Schwab, J.J. (1964). The teaching of science as enquiry. In J.J. Schwab and P.B. Brandwein (Eds.), *The Teaching of Science* (pp. 3-103). Cambridge, MA: Harvard University Press.

Science Council of Canada (1984). *Science for Every Student. Report 36.* Ottawa, On: Ministry of Supply and Services.

Segal, H. (1988). *Educating Reason.* New York: Routledge.

Seiler, G. (2001). Reversing the "Standard" direction: Science emerging from the lives of African American students. *Journal of Research in Science Teaching, 38*(9), 1000-1014.

Shavelson, R.J., Baxter, G., & Pine, J. (1992). Performance assessments: Political rhetoric and measurement reality. *Educational Researcher, 21*(4), 22-27.

Shepardson, D.P., & Britsch, S.J. (1997). Children's science journals: tools for teaching, learning, and assessing. *Science and Children, 34*(5), 13-17, 46-47.

Shulman, L.S. (1986). Those who understand: Knowledge growth in teaching. *Educational Researcher, 15*(2), 4-14.

Shulman, L.S. (1987). Knowledge and teaching foundations of a new reform. *Harvard Education Review, 57*(1), 1-22.

Smith, D.C., & Neale, D.C. (1989). The construction of subject matter knowledge in primary science teaching. *Teaching and Teacher Education, 5*(1), 1-20.

Smith, P. G. (1995). Reveling in rubrics. *Science Scope, 19*(1), 34-36.

Solano-Flores, G. & Nelson-Barber, S. (2001). On the cultural validity of science assessments. *Journal of Research in Science Teaching, 38*(5), 553-573.

Solomon, J. (1983). Learning about energy: How pupils think in two domains. *European Journal of Science Education, 5*(1), 49-59

Solomon, J. (1988). Science, technology and society courses: tools for thinking about social issues. *International Journal of Science Education, 10*(4), 379-387.

Solomon, J. (1989). The social construction of school science. In R. Millar (Ed.), *Doing Science: Images of Science in Science Education* (pp. 126-136). London: Falmer Press.

Solomon, J. (1993). *Teaching Science, Technology and Society.* Buckingham: Open University Press.

Solomon, J. (1994). The rise and fall of constructivism. *Studies in Science Education, 23*, 1-19.

Solomon, J., & Aikenhead, G. (Eds.) (1992). *STS Education: International Perspectives on Reform.* New York: Teachers College.

Stake, R., & Easley, J.A. (1978). *Case Studies in Science Education Volume I the Case Reports.* CIRCE, University of Illinois: Urbana-Champaign, IL.

Stake, R., & Easley, J.A. (1978). *Case Studies in Science Education Volume II Design, Overview and General Findings.* CIRCE, University of Illinois: Urbana-Champaign, IL.

Stepans, J. (1994). *Targeting Students' Science*

Misconceptions: Physical Science Activities Using the Conceptual Change Model. Riverview, FL: Idea Factory.

Stepans, J., Saigo, B., & Ebert, C. (1995). *Changing the Classroom from Within: Partnership, Collegiality, and Constructivism.* Montgomery, AL: Saiwood.

Strike, K., & Posner, G. (1992). A revisionist theory of conceptual change. In R. Duschl and R. Hamilton (Eds.), *Philosophy of Science, Cognitive Psychology and Educational Theory and Practice* (pp. 147-176). New York: State University of New York Press.

Sutton, C. (1989). Writing and reading in science: the hidden messages. In R. Millar (Ed.), *Doing Science: Images of Science in Science Education* (pp. 137-159). London: Falmer Press.

Sutton, C. (1996). Beliefs about science and beliefs about language. *International Journal of Science Education, 18*(1), 1-18.

Symington, D., Biddulph, F., Happs, J., and Osborne, R. (1982). *Primary School Pupils' Ideas About Rocks (Working Paper No. 107).* University of Waikato: Learning in Science Project.

Symington, D., Boundy, K., Radford, T., & Walton, J. (1981). Children's drawings of natural phenomena. *Research in Science Education, 11,* 41-50.

Tassel-Baska, J.V., & Kulieke, M.J. (1987). The role of community-based scientific resources in developing science talent: A case study. *Gifted Child Quarterly, 3,* 111-115.

Technology For All Americans Project. (1996). *A Rationale and Structure for the Study of Technology.* Reston, VA: International Technology Education Association.

The Design Council. (1995). *Definitions of Design.* London: The Design Council.

Thompson, S.J., Benson, S.N.K., Pachnowski, L.M., & Salzman, J.A. (2001). *Decision-Making in Planning and Teaching.* NY: Longman.

Tickle, L. (1990). *Design and Technology in Primary School Classrooms.* London: Falmer.

Tippins, D.J., & Dana, N.F. (1992). Culturally relevant alternative assessment. *Science Scope, 15*(6), 50-53.

Tobias, S. (1990). *They're Not Dumb, They're Different.* Tucson AR: Research Corporation.

Tobin, K., & Fraser, B. (Eds.) (1999). Exemplary Practice in Science and Mathematics Education. Perth, Australia: Curtin University.

Tobin, K. & Tippins, D. (1993). Constructivism as a referent for teaching and learning. In K. Tobin (Ed.), *The Practice of Constructivism in Science Education* (pp. 3-21). Hillsdale, NJ: Earlbaum.

Tombari, M., & Borich, G. (1999). *Authentic Assessment in the Classroom.* Upper Saddle River, NJ: Merrill.

Torrance, H. (1995). *Evaluating Authentic Assessment.* Buckingham: Open University Press.

Vincenti, W.G. (1990). *What Engineers Know and How They Know It: Analytical Studies From Aeronautical History.* Baltimore, MD: John Hopkins University Press.

Von Glaserfeld, E. (1989). Cognition, construction of knowledge, and teaching. *Synthese, 80,* 121-140.

Vygotsky, L. (1962). *Thought and Language.* Cambridge, MA: MIT Press.

Vygotsky, L. (1968). *Mind in Society.* Cambridge, MA: Harvard University Press.

Warren, B., Ballenger, C., Ogonowski, M., Roseberry, A.S., & Hudicourt-Barnes, J. (2001). Rethinking diversity in learning science: The logic of everyday languages. Unpublished manuscript.

Weiss, I.R. (1978). *Report of the 1977 National Survey of Science, Mathematics, and Social Studies Education.* Center for Education Research and Evaluation: Research Triangle Park, NC.

White, R., & Gunstone, R. (1992). *Probing Understanding.* London: Falmer Press.

Wiggins, G. (1989). A true test: Toward more authentic and equitable assessment. *Phi Delta Kappan,* 49(8), 35-37.

Wiggins, G. (1992). Creating tests worth taking. *Educational Leadership,* 49(8), 26-34.

Williams, P. & Jinks, D. (1985). *Design and Technology 5–12.* London: Falmer.

Wolf, A. (1995). Authentic assessments in a competitive sector: institutional prerequisites and cautionary tales. In H. Torrance (Ed.), *Evaluating Authentic Assessment* (pp. 88-104). Buckingham: Open University Press.

Worthen, B. (1993). Critical issues that will determine the future alternative assessment. *Phi Delta Kappan,* 74(6), 450-454.

Yager, R. (1990). STS: Thinking over the years. *The Science Teacher,* 57(3), 52-55.

Yager, R. (1991). The constructivist learning model. *The Science Teacher,* 58(6), 52-57.

Yore, L.D. (2000). Enhancing science literacy for all students with embedded reading instruction and writing-to-learn activities. *Journal of Deaf Studies and Deaf Education,* 5, 105-122.

Zahorik, J.A. (1997). Encouraging – and challenging – students' understandings. *Educational Leadership,* 54(6), 30-32.

Appendix A
Handling and Storing Materials Safely

Prior to each class you teach, you should try out the activity you intend for the students and think carefully about any safety issues that might arise. You should always set a good example by wearing eye protection when appropriate (disinfect goggles between use), using a teacher demonstration rather than a student hands–on activity if there is any concern about safety (e.g., open candle flame), and having parent volunteers present to assist young students with some tools (e.g., glue guns). Safety rules and charts should be posted and reviewed with the students at intervals throughout the year. A fire extinguisher, first aid kit, and hand protection (beware of allergies to latex gloves) should be made available to the students. Electrical outlets should be grounded and no extension cords should cross aisles where students might walk.

Supplies such as vinegar, food coloring, and batteries should be stored in locked storage cabinets and checked regularly for spills or leakage. Check with provincial laws that govern safe handling and storage of materials to learn what you should and should not bring into a classroom.

In some technology classes you may plan for students to use tools such as scissors, hacksaws, hand drills, glue guns, and hole punches. Before allowing students to use these tools, guide them through several lessons on how to use these tools correctly and safely. Students will need instruction on how to hold tools properly, how to use them safely, and how to select the right tool for the job. For example, a hacksaw should be used to cut wood and should not be used with cardboard or paper products. When drilling into wood, brad-tipped drill bits allow students to stabilize drills prior to drilling. C–clamps and bench hooks can also help steady wood prior to drilling and cutting. Glue gun glue (even from cool melt guns) can burn if allowed to drop onto exposed skin.

In order to practice safe procedures for using and handling materials and design a safe classroom environment, you should consult local guidelines and then access information that has been compiled by science safety experts.

Selected Readings

National Science Teachers Association (1978). *Safety in the Elementary Science Classroom.* Arlington, VA: NSTA.

The authors provide accessible information about steps to take in event of a classroom accident or injury. Also included are ideas about caring for animals and plants and how to safely use equipment and materials.

Selected Websites

MANITOBA SCIENCE SAFETY
http://www.edu.gov.mb.ca/ks4/docs/support/scisafe/
This website contains comprehensive information for science safety in the classroom.
Science Safety General Guidelines

SCIENCE SAFETY GENERAL GUIDELINES
http://csss.enc.org/safety
This website lists safety guidelines for classrooms.

COUNCIL OF SCIENCE SUPERVISORS
http://csss.enc.org
This website provides information about handling materials in the classroom.

ALBERTA EDUCATION – SAFETY IN THE SCIENCE CLASSROOM (CONSULTATION DRAFT, 2004)
http://www.education.gov.ab.ca/k%5F12/curriculum /bySubject/science/
This consultation draft contains a variety of useful information about handling safety issues in science classrooms.

Appendix B
Living Organisms in the Classroom

As you plan your science units, especially those based on the life sciences, you may want to bring live plants and animals into your classroom. Before bringing live organisms into the classroom, you should consider the following:

- **Why am I bringing live plants and animals into the classroom?** What learning goals can only be accomplished through bringing live plants and animals into the classroom? Could the same learning goals be met through other means (e.g., field trips)? Will the plant or animal integrate well with curriculum goals?

- **Am I willing to assume ultimate responsibility for the plants and animals?** Although children can assist with caring for the plants and animals, sustained care often becomes the responsibility of the teacher. Who cleans up – are custodians willing? Who will take pets home on weekends and holidays? How will the organisms be evacuated during a fire drill? Who is economically responsible for purchasing food, supplying a habitat, and paying for veterinary bills? What will you do and say if the pet dies? What will you do if the pets breed? What will you do if the pet escapes? Who will be responsible for feeding and cleaning routines? What will you do if you have heated fish tanks and a power outage occurs?

- **Do I have good background knowledge of the plant or animal?** How long does the organism live? How big will it get? What is the natural habitat of the organism? What is the proper care for the organisms? Are you considering an exotic or endangered species? (These species are absolutely not recommended for classroom use.)

- **Can I create a habitat for the plant or animal that resembles their natural habitat?** Do you have a quiet space with sufficient sunlight that is away from drafts

and has adequate moisture and temperature? Can you ensure the animal or plant will be exposed to little handling? Does the animal have a retreat from activity within the habitat? Can you develop rules for handling the pet?

- **Does the plant or animal present any threat to students?** Do any of your students have allergies to feathers and fur? (You should send a note home to the parents prior to bringing animals into classroom.) Are there any diseases associated with the plant or animal (e.g., harmful microorganisms in pond water; salmonella infections in turtles)? Can you arrange for a veterinary examination prior to bringing any animals into the classroom?

Should you decide that you do want to bring plants and animals into your classroom, teaching resources and biological supply companies have much information available to inform and assist.

Selected Websites

FOSS PLANT AND ANIMAL CARE
http://lhsfoss.org/fossweb/teachers/materials/plantanimal.html#m
This website provides information about how to care for plants and animals in the classroom.

CAROLINA BIOLOGICAL CARE CARDS
http://www.carolina.com/how_do_i/classroom_critters.asp
This website features how to care for a variety of plants and animals in the classroom

Appendix C
Purchasing Classroom Materials

As you plan a variety of science and technology activities for the diverse students in your classroom, you will also have to manage materials commonly used in these activities. Many good teaching resources provide lists of materials that you should collect and store in your science classroom. Figure C-1 lists some of these common materials and shows a variety of materiaAs you plan a variety of materials that can be collected by supportive parents.

A letter sent home to parents at the beginning of the school year that lists items to possibly donate is a way of quickly involving parents in your science program.

Some tools and materials will need to be purchased. Whenever possible, purchase these supplies at a local hardware, hobby, or department store. Should some specialized materials be unavailable (e.g., microcubes), you will need to purchase these materials from a reputable science and technology supply company.

Selected Websites

TECHNOLOGY TEACHING SYSTEMS
http://www.tts.ca
This website features materials and supplies that assist to teach science and technology activities.

NORTHWEST SCIENTIFIC
http://www.nwscience.com
This website provides information and materials that can be used to teach science topics.

CAROLINA BIOLOGICAL
http://www.carolina.com
This website features materials used to teach science topics and also features a selection of teaching resources full of activity ideas to use with children.

Figure C-1
Science and Technology Materials

Science and Technology Support Materials Collected From Homes		
toilet rolls	paper towel rolls	cardboard boxes
egg cartons	milk cartons	plastic bags
cardboard	aluminum plates	wood scraps
spools	clothes pegs	plastic containers
plastic lids	film canisters	berry baskets
twist ties	tin cans	plastic blocks
newspaper	dry cleaning bags	plastic bags
plastic tubing	soda cans	plastic soda bottles
large glass jars	small glass jars (baby food)	aquarium
metal spoons	aluminum tart plates	metal washers

Science and Technology Support Materials Which Will Need to be Purchased or Donated From Parents		
sand paper	carpenter's glue	toothpicks
stir sticks	tongue depressors	string
brass fasteners	pipe cleaners	model clay
art straws	wheels	paper clips
tape	corks	wood
rubber bands	meager motors	batteries
wire	battery holders	balloons
cloth	nylon fishing line	candles
wooden dowels	plastic straws	thread
growing media	tacks	aluminum foil
iron nails	compasses	plastic bags
flashlight bulbs	gears	pulleys
magnets	marbles	magnifying lens
microcubes	thermometers	wax paper

Science and Technology Tools to be Purchased		
hammers	nails	safety glasses
saw blades	junior hacksaws	bench hooks
cool melt glue guns	glue sticks	clamps
drills	brad tipped drill bits	Jax joiners
utility scissors	rulers	hole punch

Appendix D
Print Resources for Teaching

Selecting Teaching Resources

Reading curriculum documents, and the range of goals and topics contained therein, can be an overwhelming experience for beginning teachers. How can you possibly come to know the science content and then create exciting activities for your students? Rest assured that this is a daunting task even for experienced teachers, however, when it comes to creating student activities, you do not have to reinvent the wheel. All teachers use teaching resources to help them understand science content and create motivating lessons for their students. What you need to know is that not all teaching resources are worth purchasing and you must be able to evaluate resources that are marketed to you as the latest must have resource.

First, why is it important to think about the selection of teaching resources? Teaching resources direct class curriculum, define the accuracy of science knowledge imparted, influence the professional development of teachers, and affect the educational roles of parents (NRC, 1999). Clearly, teaching resources that you use can have a great influence on how your students think about and understand science, how professional development is designed for teachers, and on how parents may or may not work with their children. With such a widespread influence, it is important to consider how resources can be used and evaluated.

Some possible approaches to using teaching resources are to follow them exactly as written (the recipe approach) or to tailor them to suit your purposes. Most teachers use the second approach as this allows them to use their professional knowledge to be an informed and creative interpreter and evaluator. In these roles, teachers can adapt resource ideas to program expectations and the specific needs of students in their classrooms. Teachers can modify suggested instructional strategies to match their preferred teaching style and better help students learn. Tailoring a resource also allows teachers to evaluate and modify the view of teaching and learning in the resource and reflect on any resource biases. For example, many stakeholders or groups with vested interests (e.g., industry groups, environmental organizations, and government departments) may provide low cost or free teaching resources in the hope of disseminating their views to students. Through tailoring the resource, you can provide students with a more balanced view of complex issues.

Figure D-1

Evaluating Teaching Resources

Information for Teachers

- Does the resource provide background science information that helps teachers understand science content?
- Does the resource provide safety information related to individual activities?
- Does the resource list affordable materials used in the lessons and clear instructions for using those materials?
- Does the resource provide ideas for integrating the lesson with other subject areas?
- Does the resource provide information about other related teaching resources?

Learning goals

- Does the resource incorporate a science/technology/society approach to teaching?
- Are the activities designed to be sensitive to the diversity of students (e.g., ethnic and cognitive diversity, and free of economic, age, and gender bias)?
- Does the resource reflect an accurate view of the nature of science?
- Are the lessons designed to help students develop concepts, skills, and attitudes?
- Does the resource feature a balance between content and process?
- Are the activities designed to allow students to revisit a concept within a number of different contexts?
- Does the resource recognize that learning takes time?
- Does the resource contain ideas for extending the students' learning beyond the scope of the lesson?

Instructional and Assessment Strategies

- Do the activities emphasize a combination of physical and mental activity?
- Are the activities designed to take into account students' ideas?
- Do the activities provide for many opportunities for the students to talk and write about their ideas?
- Are the activities sequenced in such a way as to encourage students to make links between activities?
- Does the resource feature a variety of instructional strategies (e.g., teacher–led demonstrations, student–led investigations, strategies to explore students' ideas, and different ways of grouping students)?
- Does the resource provide practical ideas for assessing students' work (e.g., activity sheets, teacher questions, performance assessments, rubrics, and examples of students' work)

In Alberta, the provincial government has compiled a list of recommended resources for teaching the elementary science program. Teachers use this list to purchase teaching materials for classrooms. Frequently, however, teachers will encounter additional teaching resources at teachers' conventions, conferences and bookstores that appear interesting. In these situations, teachers must evaluate the resources to determine their appropriateness for use in their classrooms. The National Research Council (1999) and the National Science Resources Center (1997) have developed tools for evaluating science teaching resources. These tools consist of questions teachers should ask when evaluating whether a teaching resource is likely to contribute to learning goals. There are three groups of evaluative questions you can ask to help you decide whether to use or purchase a teaching resource. These questions are grouped in Figure D-1.

These questions help to evaluate whether the resource is centered on one instructional strategy or whether a variety is used to assist students with diverse backgrounds and learning styles. Assessment strategies should also be varied with suggestions provided for assessing students' conceptual understanding, and skill and attitude development.

Selected Readings

Hazen, R.M. & Trefil, J. (1990). *Science Matters: Achieving Scientific Literacy.* NY: Anchor Books.

The authors provide basic information about a variety of science topics for those in need of a greater understanding of science subject matter knowledge.
National Research Council (1999). *Selected Instructional Materials.* Washington D.C.: National Academy Press.

The authors provide guidelines and worksheets to assist in selecting science instructional materials.

Six Good Science Activity Sources

Bosak, Susan (1986). *Science Is.* Ottawa: Youth Science Foundation.

Brown, Robert (1984). *333 Science Tricks and Experiments.* Fort Worth, Texas: Radio Shack.

Brown, Robert (1984). *333 More Science Tricks and*

Experiments. Fort Worth, Texas: Radio Shack.

Liem, Tik (1989). *Invitations to Science Inquiry.* California: Science Inquiry Enterprises.

Lorbeer, George (2000). *Science Activities for Elementary Students.*

Lowery, Lawrence (1985). *The Everyday Science Sourcebook.* Ontario: Spectrum.

Selected Websites

ALBERTA EDUCATION- ELEMENTARY SCIENCE AUTHORIZED RESOURCES ANNOTATED LIST (1998)
http://www.education.gov.ab.ca/k%5F12/curriculum /bySubject/science/
This website contains a list of teaching resources that are approved for Alberta.

CENTRE FOR MATHEMATICS, SCIENCE AND TECHNOLOGY EDUCATION (CMASTE)
http://www.ioncmaste.ca/homepage/index.html
This website features a list of curriculum resources, some of which can be used to teach Alberta elementary science topics.

ACTIVITIES INTEGRATING MATH AND SCIENCE (AIMS)
http://www.aimsedu.org/
This website features a great teaching resource consisting of classroom activities on a variety of science topics.

GREAT EXPLORATIONS IN MATH AND SCIENCE (GEMS)
http://www.lhs.berkeley.edu/GEMS/
This website features an exceptional teaching resource consisting of classroom activities on a variety of science topics.

FULL OPTION SCIENCE SYSTEM (FOSS)
http://lhsfoss.org/
This website features a great teaching resource consisting of classroom activities on a variety of science topics.

SCIENCE AND TECHNOLOGY FOR CHILDREN (STC)
http://www.si.edu.nsrc/pubs/stc/overv.htm
This website features the STC series that is published by Carolina Biological Supply Company in North Carolina.